Math Practice
the Singapore Way

Grade 1

Marshall Cavendish
Education

Published by Marshall Cavendish Education

Marshall Cavendish Corp.
99 White Plains Road
Tarrytown, NY 10591
Website: www.marshallcavendish.us/edu

Originally published as Maths Practice Papers © 2002 Times Media Private Limited, © 2003, 2010 Marshall Cavendish International (Singapore) Private Limited, © 2014 Marshall Cavendish Education Pte Ltd

First published 2012
Reprinted 2016, 2018, 2020 (twice)

Other Marshall Cavendish Offices:
Marshall Cavendish International (Asia) Private Limited, 1 New Industrial Road, Singapore 536196 • Marshall Cavendish International (Thailand) Co Ltd. 253 Asoke, 12th Flr, Sukhumvit 21 Road, Klongtoey Nua, Wattana, Bangkok 10110, Thailand • Marshall Cavendish (Malaysia) Sdn Bhd, Times Subang, Lot 46, Subang Hi-Tech Industrial Park, Batu Tiga, 40000 Shah Alam, Selangor Darul Ehsan, Malaysia.

Marshall Cavendish is a registered trademark of Times Publishing Limited

ISBN 978-0-7614-8033-4

Printed in Singapore

Introduction

Mathematics the Singapore Way is a term coined to refer to the textbook series used in Singapore schools. Mathematics the Singapore Way focuses on problem solving, given that is it based on a curriculum framework that has mathematical problem solving as its focus. Mathematics the Singapore Way also focuses on thinking, given that the Singapore education system is driven by the *Thinking Schools, Learning Nation* philosophy. Mathematics the Singapore Way is also based on learning theories that provide clear directions on how mathematics is learned and should be taught.

Singapore mathematics textbooks, initial teacher preparation, and the subsequent professional development for teachers are based on helping teachers understand what to teach in mathematics and how to teach it.

While these books are not part of the formal classroom program, they provide selected groups of students with the necessary consolidation of skills. Some students require more opportunities to consolidate their basic concepts and skills, and these books are written with that goal in mind. Such learning materials, if they are prepared consistently with the fundamentals of Mathematics the Singapore Way, help learners review basic concepts through the use of visuals. In some cases, it may be necessary for some learners also to have access to concrete materials. It should be noted that good practice is not a matter merely of random repetition. Learners must be helped through careful scaffolding. Good practice consists of careful variations in the tasks learners are given.

I hope this series of books is able to provide the necessary help for learners who need to be challenged beyond basic concepts and skills.

Yeap Ban Har
Marshall Cavendish Institute

Preface

Mathematics the Singapore Way is a series of five books with exercises that adhere closely to the latest Math syllabus in Singapore.

The topics in this book are carefully arranged to follow the sequence of the topics in the students' basic texts, thus enabling them to use the exercises as further practice to gain mastery of mathematical skills. The exercises can also be used to supplement teachers with a thorough and reliable program of testing that provides information for necessary re-teaching.

In mathematics, constant review of concepts is essential. Therefore, the built-in revision exercises will refresh students' memories so that no basic skills or concepts will be forgotten.

The variety of sample exam questions found in the final tests at the end of the book will help pupils face their final math tests with confidence.

Notes pages are provided at the back of the book for those who require more space to work out solutions to the problems.

Contents

Math Practice the Singapore Way

UNIT 1 Notes

Concept: Numbers to 10

zero (0) one (1) two (2) three (3) four (4)

five (5) six (6) seven (7)

eight (8) nine (9) ten (10)

Concept: More, Fewer, Same

○○○ ☆☆☆ □□

There are **more** ___○___ than ___□___ .

There are **fewer** ___□___ than ___☆___ .

The number of ___○___ and the number of ___☆___ are the **same**.

Concept: Largest and Smallest

0 1 2 3 4 5 6 7 8 9 10

10 is the largest number.

0 is the smallest number.

1. Count the faces and then color the same number of hats. [1]

2. Count the dots and then color the same number of kites. [1]

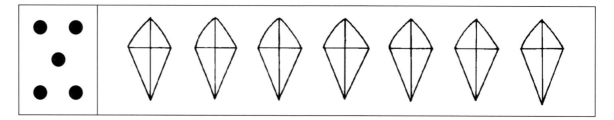

3. Circle the two sets that have the same number of fish. [1]

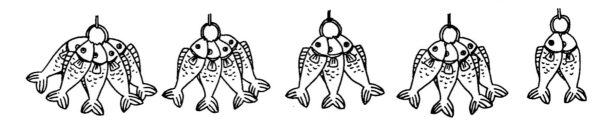

4. Color the correct number of pitchers. [1]

| 3 | |

5. Check (✓) the correct set. [1]

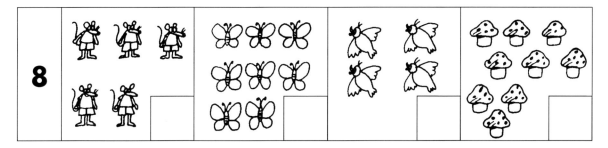

| 8 | |

6. Count and write the correct number. [1]

7. Count and write the correct number. [1]

8. Count and circle the correct number in each set. [1]

3   5   4

9   7   6

9.   Check (✓) the set that has **more**.   [1]

10. Check (✓) the set that has **fewer**.   [1]

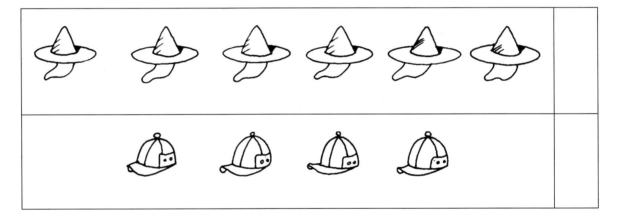

11. Color the set that has **fewer**.   [1]

12. Color the set that has **more**. [1]

13. Color 7 dogs. [1]

14. Color 5 birds. [1]

Fill in the missing numbers. [5]

15.

16.

17.

18.

19. Join the numbers in order. [1]

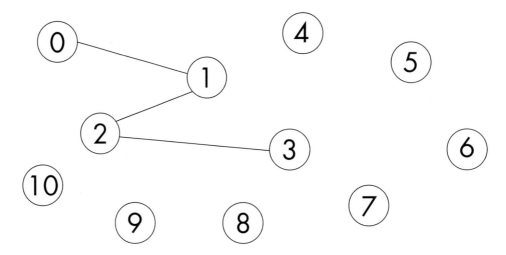

Write the numbers in the boxes. [2]

20.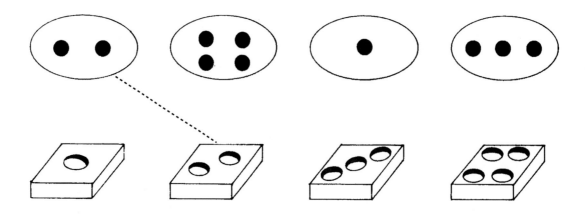

21.

22. Match the items in both sets. [1]

© 2012 Marshall Cavendish Corporation

23. Count and write the correct number of flowers. [2]

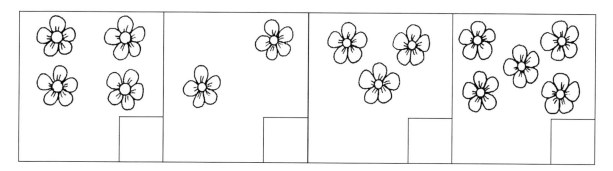

24. Match the numbers with their names. [4]

| two | seven | five | nine | zero | six | eight | ten |

25. Arrange these numbers in order, starting with the largest number. [2]

(1)   (4)   (2)   (5)

——————, ——————, ——————, ——————
largest

26. Write the smallest number in the box. [2]

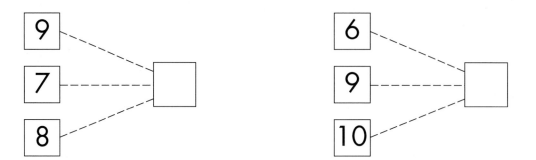

27. Check (✓) the set that has **fewer than**

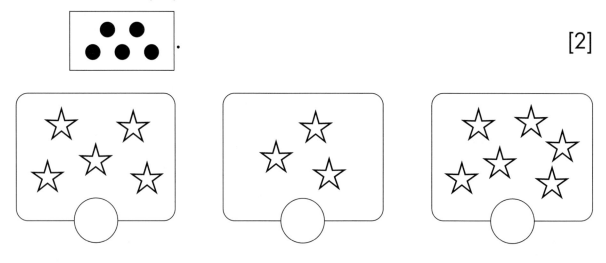

[2]

28. Check (✓) the set that has **more than**

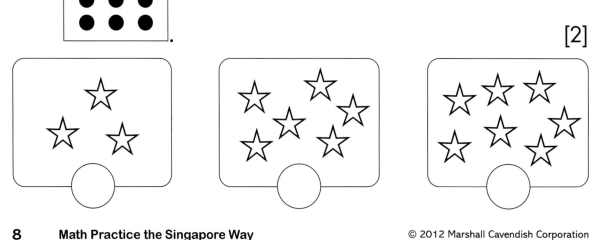

[2]

29. Which set is more? Which is fewer?　　　[2]

| hands | | | | | gloves |

There are more _____ than _____.

There are fewer _____ than _____.

30.

| carrots | rabbits | same |　　　[5]

How many rabbits are there in all? _____

How many carrots are there? _____

The number of _____ and the number of _____ are the _____.

31. Fill in the blanks.　　　[6]

(a) 1 more than 6 is _____.

(b) 1 less than 8 is _____.

(c) _____ is 1 more than 5.

(d) _____ is 1 more than 9.

(e) _____ is 1 less than 8.

(f) _____ is 1 less than 6.

Concept: Composing Numbers

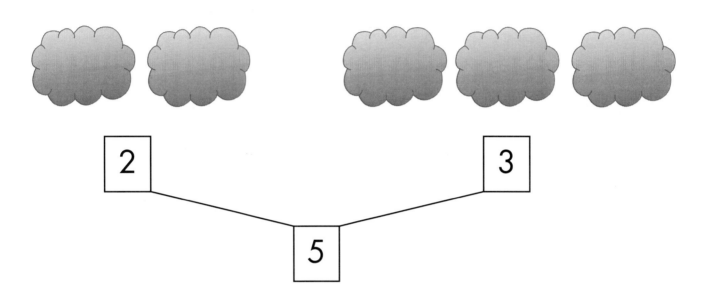

Concept: Decomposing Numbers

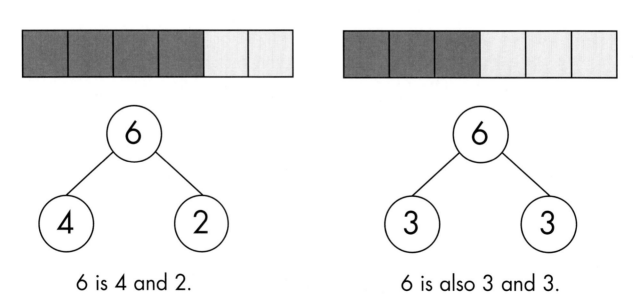

6 is 4 and 2.   6 is also 3 and 3.

Number Bonds

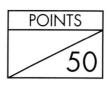
1. Fill in the correct numbers. [4]

	Total	🍎	🍊
🍎🍎🍎🍎🍎🍊🍊	7		
🍎🍎🍎🍎🍊🍊🍊	7		
🍎🍎🍎🍎🍎🍊🍊	7		
🍎🍎🍎🍎🍎🍊	7		

2. Color the shapes as shown by the numbers in the table. [4]

	Total	Red	Blue
○○○○○	5	3	2
△△△△△△	6	2	4
▢▢▢▢▢▢▢	7	4	3
◇◇◇◇	4	3	1

3. Draw a line to separate each set into two parts to match the numbers below. [2]

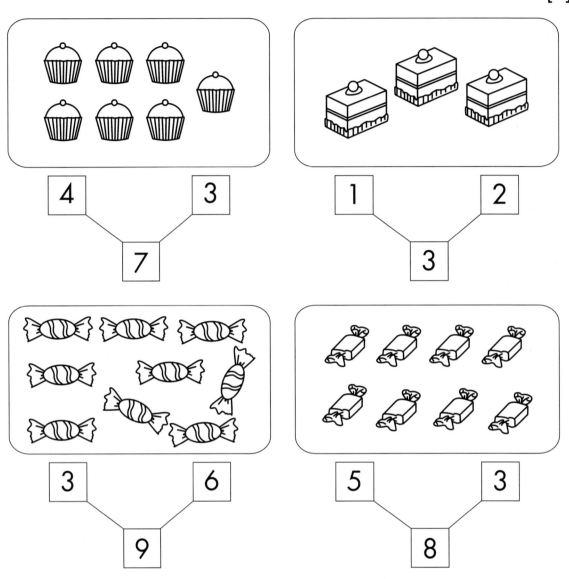

4. Draw a line to join each cup to a saucer to make 6. [2]

5. Join each cover with the correct teapot to equal 8.

[2]

6. Draw the missing items.   [4]

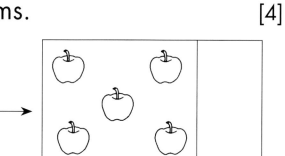

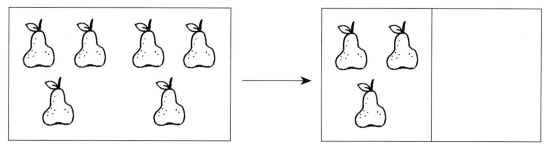

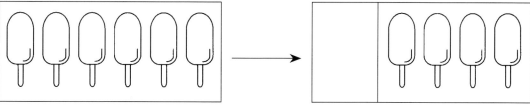

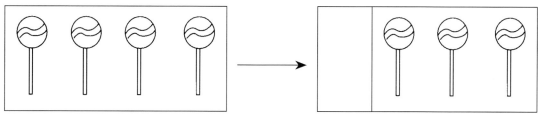

Math Practice the Singapore Way

7. Fill in the missing numbers. [2]

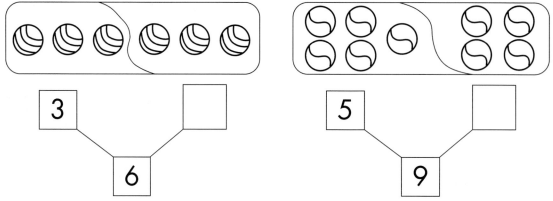

8. Color the objects that add up to the number in the box on the left. [4]

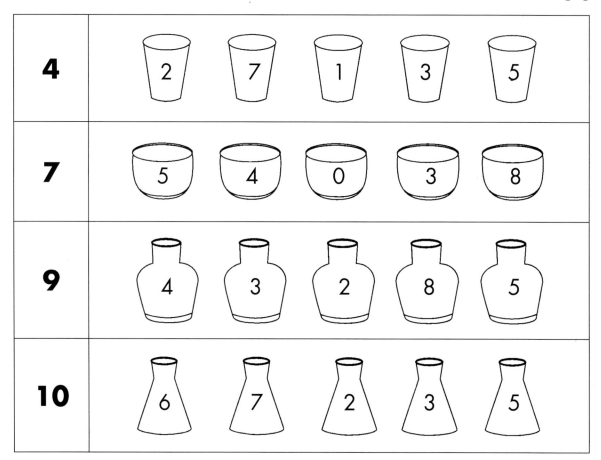

9. Fill in the missing numbers. [2]

(a)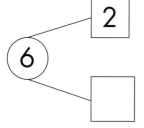

(b)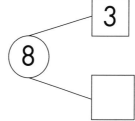

(c)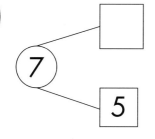

(d)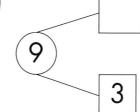

10. Fill in the missing numbers and draw the missing shapes. [4]

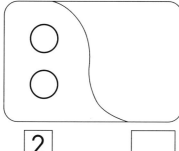

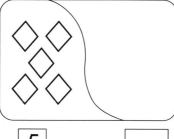

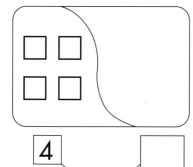

11. Look at the pictures. Then complete the number bonds.   [4]

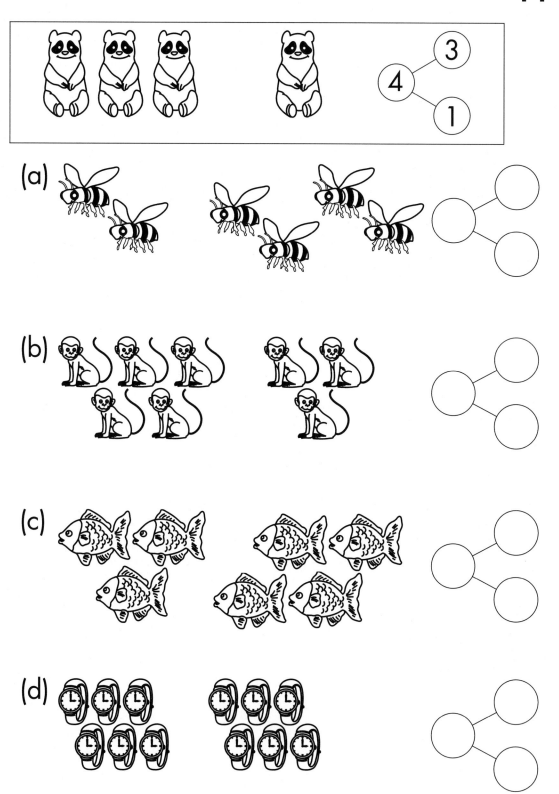

(a)

(b)

(c)

(d)

12. Use two different colors to show a pair of numbers that add up to the given number. [6]

For example,

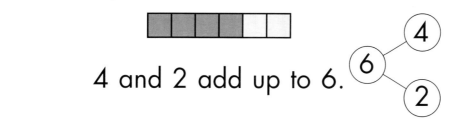

4 and 2 add up to 6.

(a)

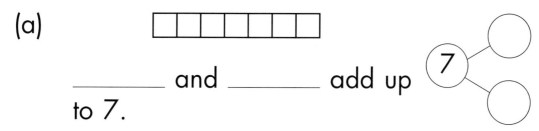

_____ and _____ add up to 7.

(b)

_____ and _____ add up to 9.

(c)

_____ and _____ add up to 10.

13. Use two different colors to show a pair of numbers that add up to 8.

Fill in the blanks and complete the number bonds. [10]

(a) ⬚⬚⬚⬚⬚⬚⬚⬚⬚

_____ and _____ add up to 8. 8

(b) ⬚⬚⬚⬚⬚⬚⬚⬚

_____ and _____ add up to 8. 8

(c) ⬚⬚⬚⬚⬚⬚⬚⬚⬚

_____ and _____ add up to 8. 8

(d) ⬚⬚⬚⬚⬚⬚⬚⬚⬚

_____ and _____ add up to 8. 8

(e) ⬚⬚⬚⬚⬚⬚⬚⬚

_____ and _____ add up to 8. 8

Notes

Concept: Counting Up from the Greater Number

It's easy to count up from 7. Think of the number 7 and put 2 fingers up. Count 7, 8, 9.

It is not easy counting up to 7 from 2. Always count up from the greater number!

Concept: 2-Step Addition

I have 2 pencils.

I have 3 more pencils. How many pencils do we have altogether?

First, count how many pencils each has. Then, count how many pencils they have altogether!

Addition within 10

1. Fill in the missing numbers. [2]

(a) 4 + _____ = ▢

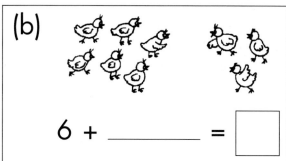

(b) 6 + _____ = ▢

2. Fill in the missing numbers. [4]

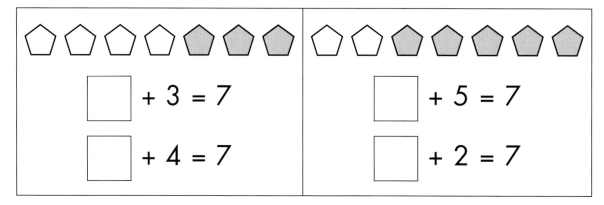

▢ + 3 = 7

▢ + 4 = 7

▢ + 5 = 7

▢ + 2 = 7

3. Color the umbrella that matches the number 8. [1]

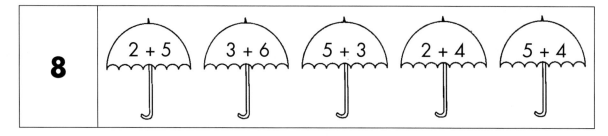

8 | 2 + 5 | 3 + 6 | 5 + 3 | 2 + 4 | 5 + 4

4. Add by counting up from the greater number. [4]

    (a) 5 + 2 = _____

    (b) 3 + 4 = _____

    (c) 6 + 2 = _____

    (d) 1 + 9 = _____

5. Write the answer in each box. [4]

1 more than 4 — 4 + 1 — 5

3 more than 5 — ☐ — ☐

2 more than 7 — ☐ — ☐

4 more than 4 — ☐ — ☐

3 more than 6 — ☐ — ☐

    Math Practice the Singapore Way

6. Complete the number bonds to show the parts and the whole.
   Then fill in the blanks.   [4]

   (a)

   _____ + _____ = _____

   (b)   _____ + 6 = 9

   △△ △△△
   △   △△△

7. Circle the number problems that make 10. [2]

   10

   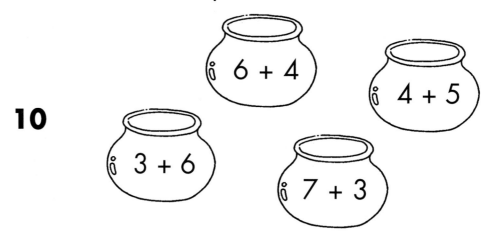

Write a number sentence using the numbers and signs given. [2]

8(a)

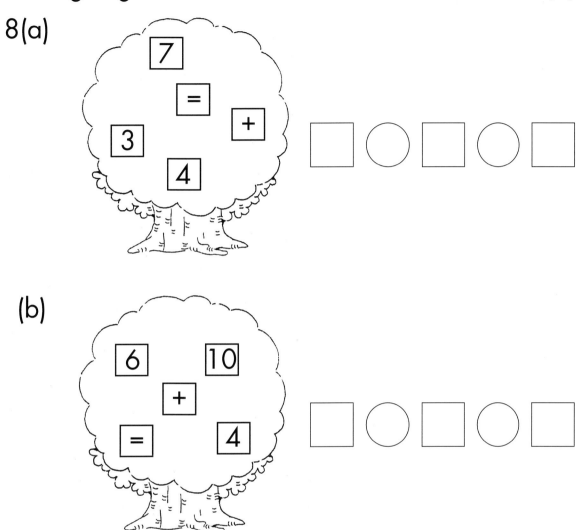

(b)

Complete the addition sentence for the pictures shown below. [16]

9(a)

_____ fish were first caught.

Another _____ fish were caught later.

☐ + ☐ = ☐

Altogether, _____ fish were caught.

(b)

There are _____ white birds.

There are _____ black birds.

There are _____ birds altogether.

(c)

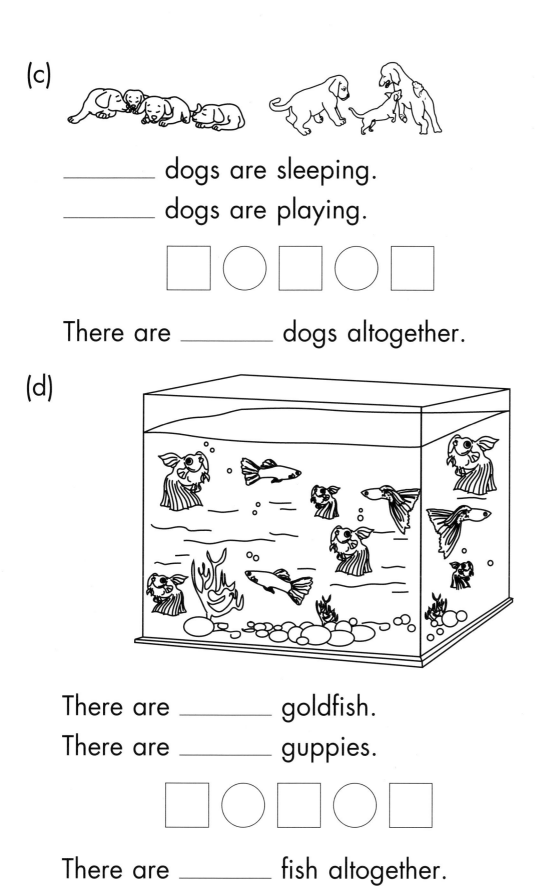

_____ dogs are sleeping.

_____ dogs are playing.

☐ ◯ ☐ ◯ ☐

There are _____ dogs altogether.

(d)

There are _____ goldfish.

There are _____ guppies.

☐ ◯ ☐ ◯ ☐

There are _____ fish altogether.

10. Solve the following word problem. [3]

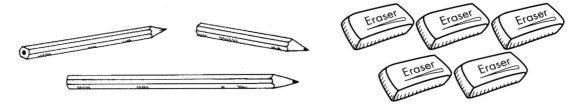

Joy has _____ pencils.

She has _____ erasers.

How many pencils and erasers does Joy have?

Joy has _____ pencils and erasers altogether.

11. Roy has 4 pairs of socks. [4]
    Jean has 1 pair more than Roy.
    How many pairs of socks do Roy and Jean have altogether?
    Show your work. (If you need additional space, use pages 167-170.)

12. Morris had 3 rabbits.
One rabbit gave birth to 2 brown and 3 gray baby rabbits.
How many rabbits does Morris have now?
Show your work.   [4]

UNIT 4 Notes

Concept: Subtraction

8 − 2 = _____

First, draw 8 items.
Then, strike out 2 items.
The remainder is the answer!

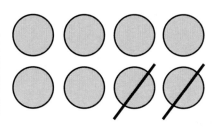

_____ − 3 = 4

First, draw 4 items.
Then, draw 3 items with lines through them.
The answer is all of the items that you have drawn!

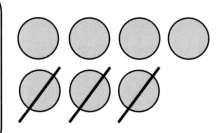

6 − _____ = 5

First, draw 6 items.
Then, strike out 5 items.
The remainder is the answer!

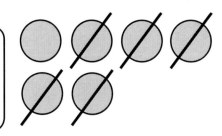

Subtraction within 10

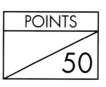
POINTS
/ 50

1. Fill in the missing numbers.   [2]

(a)

6 – 4 = ☐

(b)

9 – 4 = ☐

2. Fill in the missing numbers.   [4]

(a) ○ ○ ○ ○ ◉ ◉ ◉

7 – 3 = _____

7 – 4 = _____

(b) ○ ○ ◉ ◉ ◉ ◉ ◉

7 – 5 = _____

7 – 2 = _____

3. Color the umbrella that matches the number 5.

[1]

5   8 – 2   4 – 1   9 – 6   6 – 3   7 – 2

4. Write the answer in each box. [4]

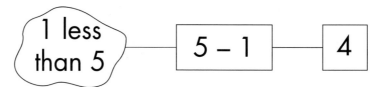

1 less than 5 — 5 – 1 — 4

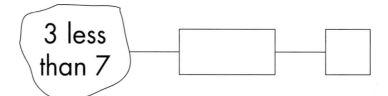

3 less than 7 — ☐ — ☐

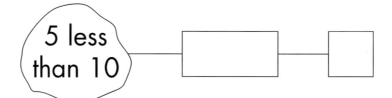

5 less than 10 — ☐ — ☐

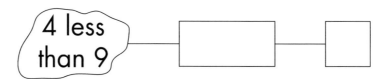

4 less than 9 — ☐ — ☐

3 less than 10 — ☐ — ☐

5. Color the shapes that equal 4. [2]

4

6 – 3   7 – 3   10 – 5   9 – 5

6. Fill in the number bond.
   Then complete the subtraction sentence. [4]

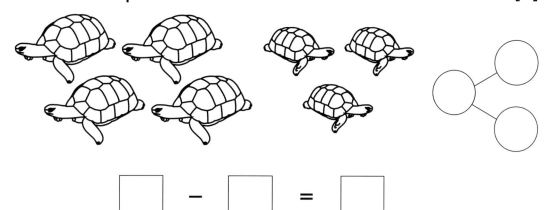

   ☐ – ☐ = ☐

7. Complete the number bonds.
   Fill in the blanks. [6]

   (a) △△△△△
       △△△△
       9 – 4 = _____

   (b) △△△△
       △△△
       _____ – 1 = 6

   (c) △△△
       △△
       5 – _____ = 5

8. Complete the subtraction sentence for each picture. [8]

(a)

There are _____ pieces of fruit.

_____ are bananas.

□ ○ □ ○ □

There are _____ pears.

(b)

There are _____ senior citizens.

_____ of the senior citizens are men.

□ ○ □ ○ □

There are _____ women.

9. There are 6 children playing together.
    Of those, 4 are boys. [3]

$$\boxed{} \bigcirc \boxed{} = \boxed{}$$

There are _____ girls.

10. There are 7 pails.
    Mary takes away 2 pails. [3]

$$\boxed{} \bigcirc \boxed{} = \boxed{}$$

_____ pails are left.

11. Kim and Jesse went to a farm to gather strawberries.

Kim gathered 8 strawberries.

Jesse gathered 6 strawberries.

How many more strawberries did Kim gather than Jesse? [3]

□ ◯ □ = □

Kim collected _____ more strawberries.

12. Look at the picture.

Make a family of number sentences. [4]

□ + □ = □   □ − □ = □

□ + □ = □   □ − □ = □

13. Fill in the blanks.
    Complete the number bonds.   [6]

(a) 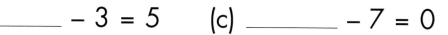 _____ – 3 = 5   (c) _____ – 7 = 0

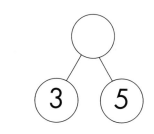   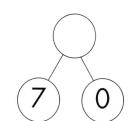

(b) 9 – _____ = 2

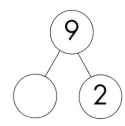

Concept: Names of Shapes

circle

triangle

square

rectangle

Concept: Size

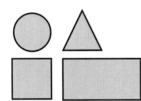
small

big

small   smaller   smallest

big   bigger   biggest

Concept: Patterns

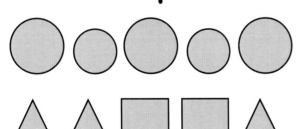

These are patterns. You can tell what comes next by looking at these patterns.

 UNIT **Shapes and Patterns**

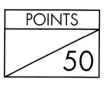
POINTS
/ 50

1. Match each object to its correct shape.　[2]

2. Color the shape that matches each object.　[2]

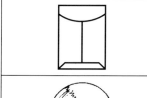　　　　

3. Color the shape that is the same size as the shaded shape.　[2]

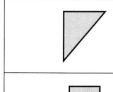　　　　

　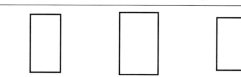

4. Check (✓) the shape that comes next.   [2]

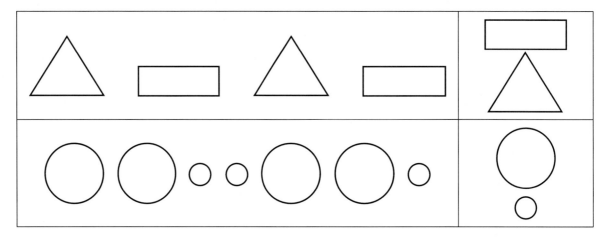
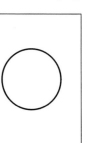

5. Color all the triangles.   [2]

There are _____ triangles.

6. Color all the squares.   [2]

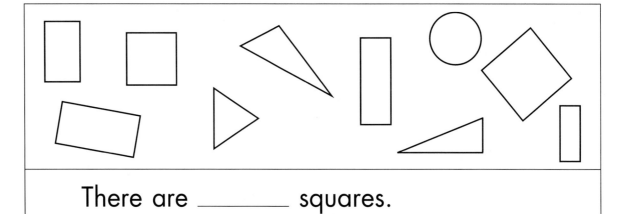

There are _____ squares.

7. Color the small circles. [2]

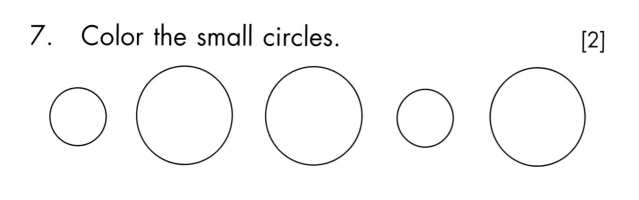

8. [2]

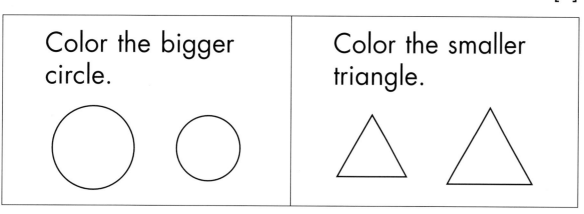

9. Part of each shape is missing.
Can you tell what shape each of them was at first?
Match each complete shape with its correct name. [4]

| triangle | | rectangle | square | | circle |

10. Color the smallest circle yellow and the biggest square blue. [2]

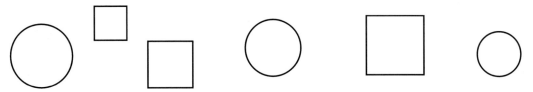

11. Color the biggest triangle green and the smallest rectangle red. [2]

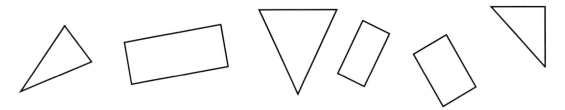

12. Study the figure.
    Then, fill in the correct number of each shape in the table. [4]

Shape	Number
circle	
rectangle	
square	
triangle	

Study each pattern.
Place a check (✓) on the shape that comes next.

13.   [1]

14.   [1]

15.   [1]

16.   [1]

17. Name the shape of the shaded part of each item. [5]

(a) 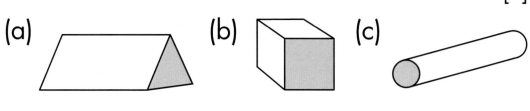 (b) (c)

_____   _____   _____

(d) 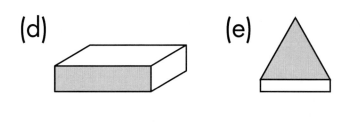 (e)

_____   _____

18. Study each pattern.
Check (✓) the solid that comes next. [4]

(a)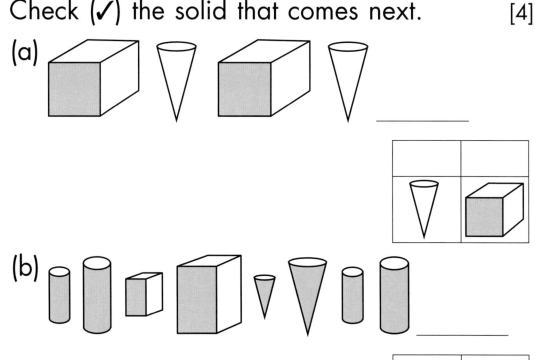

_____

(b)

_____

19. What is missing in each pattern?
    Check (✓) the correct answer.   [4]

(a) 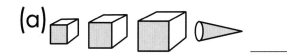 _____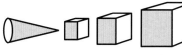

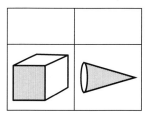

(b)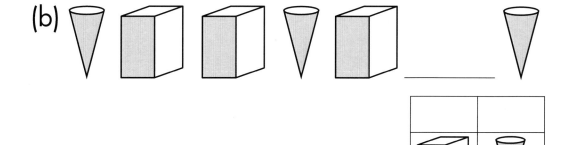

20. Study the picture carefully and fill in the blanks.   [5]

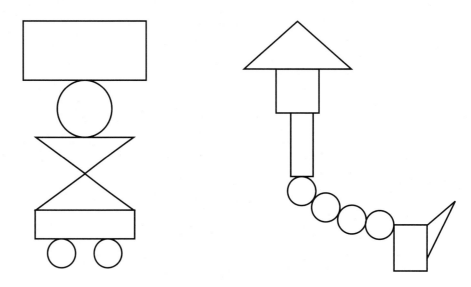

There are _____ circles.

There are _____ rectangles.

There are _____ more rectangles than squares.

There are as many triangles as _____.

There are _____ shapes altogether.

Notes

Concept: Ordinal Numbers

| 1st | 2nd | 3rd | 4th | 5th | 6th | 7th | 8th | 9th | 10th |

| 10th | 9th | 8th | 7th | 6th | 5th | 4th | 3rd | 2nd | 1st |

Concept: Before, After, and Between

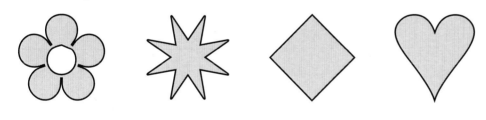

The _____ is **before** the _____ .

The _____ is **after** the _____ .

The _____ is **between** the _____ and the _____ .

Math Practice the Singapore Way

Ordinal Numbers

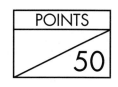
1. Color the 6th house.   [1]

1st

2. Color the 4th tree.   [1]

1st

3. Circle the 5th bird.   [1]

1st

4. Circle the 2nd duck.   [1]

1st

5. Draw a ball inside the 3rd hoop.   [1]

1st

6. Draw a fish in the 2nd fish bowl. [1]

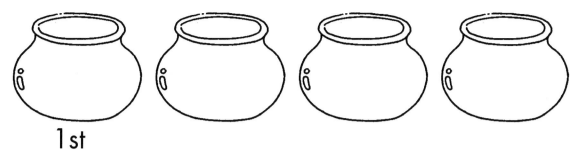

1st

7. Color the 6th pail from the left. [1]

8. Color the 8th flag from the right. [1]

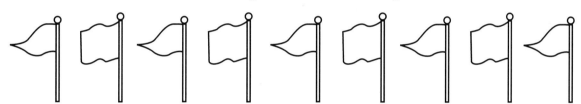

9. Write 4th, 3rd, or 1st on the arrows.
   Then, write the correct letters in the boxes. [5]

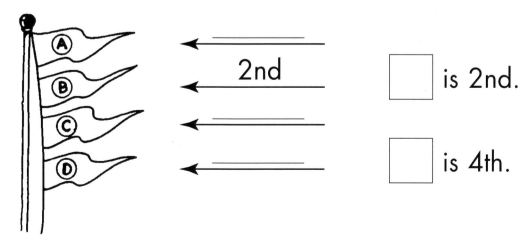

2nd

☐ is 2nd.

☐ is 4th.

10. Write 1st, 2nd, 3rd, and 4th to show the amount of water in each glass.
Go from the smallest to the greatest amount of water in the glass. [4]

_____ _____ _____ _____

11. Join the labels to show the positions of the runners. [4]

12. Write 1st, 2nd, 3rd, 4th, and 5th to show the order of steps in sketching a clown. [4]

_____   1st   _____   _____   _____

13. Look at the picture.
    Identify the beetles. [4]

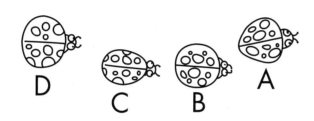

Beetle ☐ is before Beetle B.

Beetle B is after Beetle ☐.

Beetle C is between Beetle B and Beetle ☐.

Beetle D is after Beetle ☐.

Math Practice the Singapore Way

14. Look at the picture.

COUNTER

John Mary Dave Paul Jean Alice Joe Roy Sam Bob

Fill in the blanks.   [10]

   (a) Jean is _____ in line.

   (b) _____ is just before Alice.

   (c) _____ is just after Paul.

   (d) _____ is between Mary and Paul.

   (e) Roy is just before _____.

   (f) Jean is just after _____.

   (g) Sam suddenly leaves the line. Who will then
       be 6th in line? _____

   (h) How many people are between Mary and
       Sam? _____

   (i) Who is fifth from the left? _____

   (j) Who is fourth from the right? _____

15. Some people are standing in line.
    Peter is the 5th person from the left.
    He is also the 3rd person from the right.
    How many people are in line? _____ [3]

16. Look at the pattern below.

    △ ○ □ △ ○ □
           3rd

    (a) Color the 5th shape. [1]
    (b) What is the name of the 6th shape?
        _____ [1]
    (c) Draw what the 10th shape would be.

        _____ [2]

    (d) The 2nd shape is a circle ○.

        The 5th shape is a circle ○.
        The _____ shape will also be a circle
        ○. [2]
    (e) In which position will the 4th triangle be?
        _____ [2]

Concept: Numbers 11 to 20

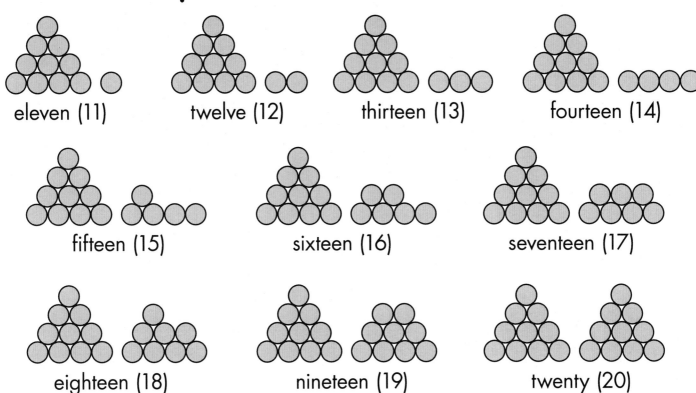

eleven (11) twelve (12) thirteen (13) fourteen (14)

fifteen (15) sixteen (16) seventeen (17)

eighteen (18) nineteen (19) twenty (20)

Concept: Tens and Ones

11 is **1 ten** (⬡) and **1 one** (○).

12 is **1 ten** and **2 ones**.

13 is **1 ten** and **3 ones**.

14 is **1 ten** and **4 ones**.

15 is **1 ten** and **5 ones**.

16 is **1 ten** and **6 ones**.

17 is **1 ten** and **7 ones**.

18 is **1 ten** and **8 ones**.

19 is **1 ten** and **9 ones**.

20 is **2 tens** and **0 ones**.

UNIT

Numbers to 20

1. Match the marbles with the correct number. [4]

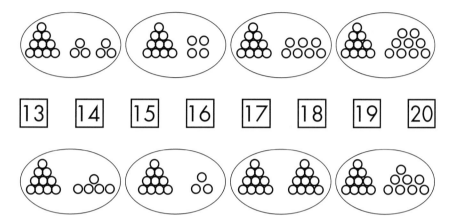

2(a) Write the correct number in each box. [2]

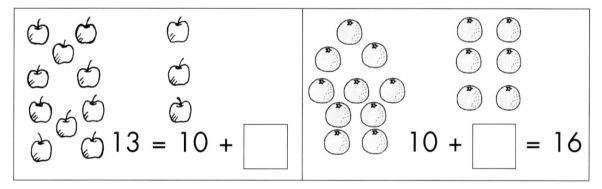

$13 = 10 +$ ▢ $10 +$ ▢ $= 16$

(b) Write the correct number in each box. [2]

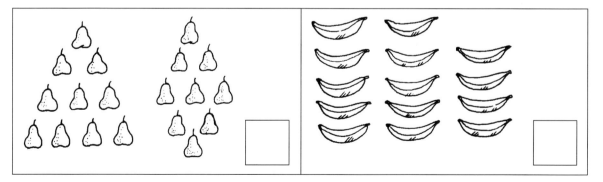

3. Match the number names to the correct numbers. [5]

| eighteen | zero | fourteen | nineteen | sixteen |

0   16   18   14   19

4. Write the correct numbers. [2]

twenty =	fifteen =
thirteen =	twelve =

5. Fill in the missing numbers. [5]

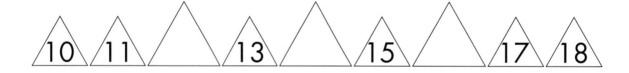

6. Write the numbers in order. [2]

——————, ——————, ——————, ——————
smallest

7. Circle the smaller of the two numbers in the boxes. [2]

15 14   18 19

8. Circle the biggest number.   [1]

| 16 | 14 | 18 | 17 | 13 | 11 | 15 | 12 |

Color ten objects. Then complete the boxes.

9.

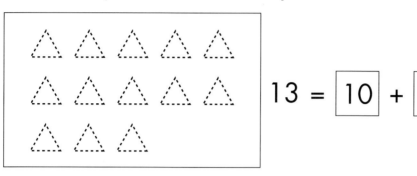

13 = 10 + □

[1]

10.

15 = 10 + □

[1]

11.

10 + □ = □

[1]

12. Color the correct number of circles.   [1]

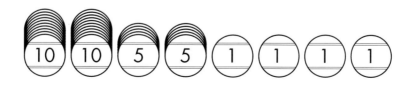

Complete the following.   [1]

13.

10 and ☐ make ☐ .

14.

Tray A   Tray B

Tray ☐ has more eggs.

Tray ☐ has ☐ fewer eggs than Tray ☐ . [4]

Complete the following:

15. ☐ is 10 more than 7.   [1]

16. 15 is 3 less than ☐ .   [1]

17. 12 is the same as

Tens	Ones

[1]

18. 20 is the same as

Tens	Ones

[1]

19. 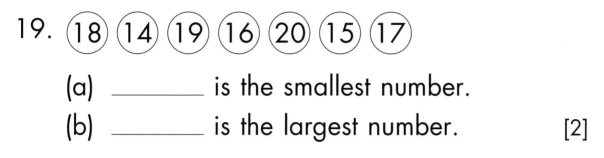 ⑱ ⑭ ⑲ ⑯ ⑳ ⑮ ⑰

(a) _____ is the smallest number.

(b) _____ is the largest number. [2]

20. Complete the number patterns. [10]

(a) ⑦ — ⑨ — ◯ — ⑬ — ⑮ — ◯

(b) 19 — 17 — ☐ — ☐ — 11 — 9

(c) ⑯ — ⑭ — ◯ — ⑩ — ◯ — ⑥

(d) 6 — 9 — ☐ — 15 — ☐

(e) △1 △2 △ △7 △11 △

21. Complete the following.   [2]

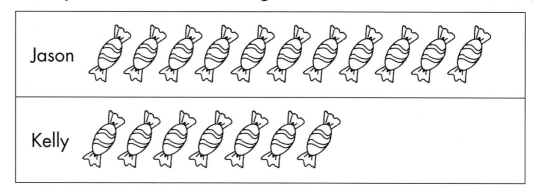

Jason

Kelly

[ ] has more sweets.

Jason can give Kelly [ ] sweets so that both
of them will have the same number of sweets.

[2]

© 2012 Marshall Cavendish Corporation

Notes

Concept: Making Groups of 10 to Add

7 + 8 = _____

First, draw 7 items and 8 items.
Next, make a group of 10.
Then, count on from 10.
10, 11, 12, 13, 14, 15.

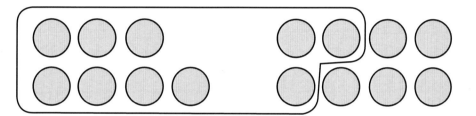

Concept: Subtracting within 20

17 - 4 = _____

First, draw 17 items. Next, strike out
4 items. Then, make a group of 10.
Finally, count on from 10. 10, 11, 12, 13.

If there are not
enough items to
make a group of
10, simply count
on from 0.

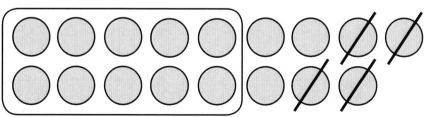

Addition and Subtraction within 20

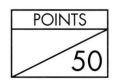
1. Add or subtract. Then fill in the blanks. [8]

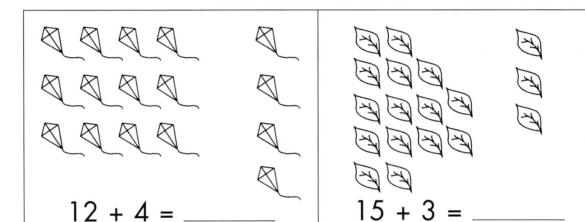

12 + 4 = _____

15 + 3 = _____

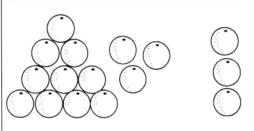

13 + 3 = _____

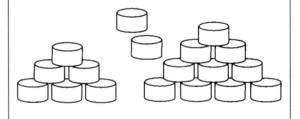

6 + 12 = _____

15 – 5 = _____

18 – 6 = _____

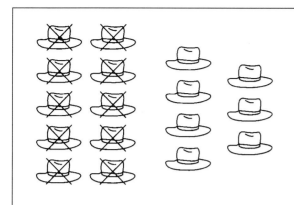

17 − 10 = _____

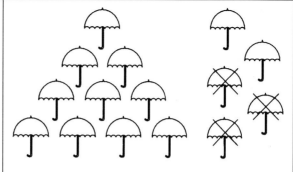

15 − _____ = _____

2. Write **+** or **−** in each circle.   [8]

(a) 14 ◯ 8 = 6   (b) 10 ◯ 3 = 13

(c) 12 ◯ 3 = 15   (d) 19 ◯ 9 = 10

(e)   7 ◯ 8 = 15   (f) 17 ◯ 3 = 20

(g) 15 ◯ 7 = 8   (h) 14 ◯ 5 = 9

3. Make a group of 10. Then add.   [4]

(a) 8 + _____ = _____   (b) 7 + _____ = _____

4. Regroup the pictures into tens and ones. Then subtract. [4]

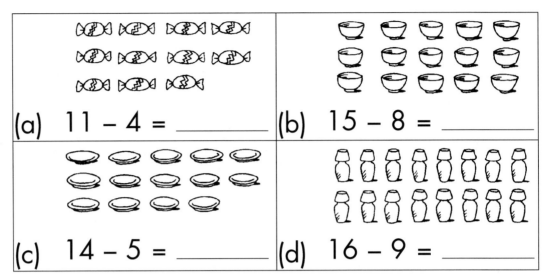

(a) 11 – 4 = _____

(b) 15 – 8 = _____

(c) 14 – 5 = _____

(d) 16 – 9 = _____

5. Match each addition and subtraction sentence to the correct answer. [6]

| 15 – 8 | | 4 + 9 | | 13 – 7 |

⬡ 12   ⬡ 13   ⬡ 6   ⬡ 7   ⬡ 18   ⬡ 8

| 5 + 7 | | 14 – 6 | | 9 + 9 |

6. Fill in the boxes with the correct answers. [8]

(a) 6 + 8 = ☐

(b) 15 – 9 = ☐

(c) 7 + 7 = ☐

(d) 13 – 8 = ☐

(e) 5 + 9 = ☐

(f) 16 – 8 = ☐

(g) 9 + 3 = ☐

(h) 14 – 6 = ☐

7. [4]

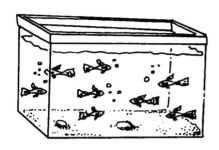 

Al has 14 guppies.
He puts 8 of them in a tank and the rest in a fishbowl.
How many guppies are in the fishbowl?

▢ ◯ ▢ = ▢

_____ guppies are in the fishbowl.

8. David has 9 marbles. [4]
His brother has 7 marbles.
How many marbles do they have altogether?

▢ ◯ ▢ = ▢

They have _____ marbles altogether.

9. Alice baked 15 cookies.
   She gave 6 to her neighbor and ate 2 herself.
   How many cookies did she have left?   [4]

   ☐ ◯ ☐ ◯ ☐ = ☐

   She had _____ cookies left.

Concept: Comparing Lengths

short

shorter

shortest

long

longer

longest

Concept: Comparing Heights

short

shorter

shortest

tall

taller

tallest

1. Which is shorter? Color it.   [2]

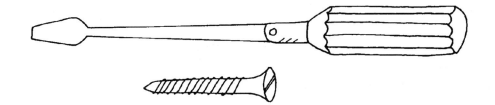

2. Color the longer brush.   [2]

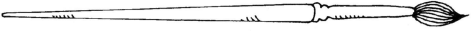

3. Draw a shorter chain.   [2]

4. Draw a longer drinking straw.   [2]

5. Color the shortest pencil. [2]

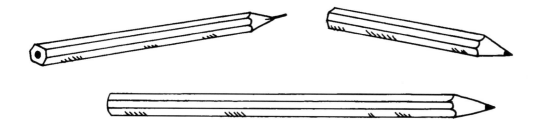

6. Color the longest umbrella. [2]

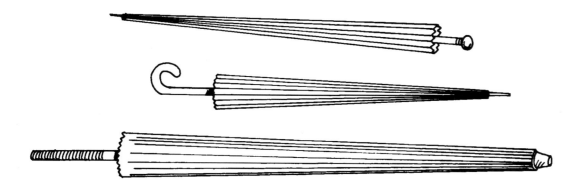

7. Color the taller boy. [2]

8. Color the shorter dog. [2]

9. Color the shortest stool. [2]

10. Color the tallest bottle. [2]

11. Fill in the blanks with **taller**, **tallest**, **shorter**, or **shortest**. [8]

sparrow   elephant   dog   giraffe

(a) The elephant is _____ than the dog.

(b) The sparrow is the _____.

(c) The dog is _____ than the elephant.

(d) The _____ animal is the giraffe.

Fill in the blanks.

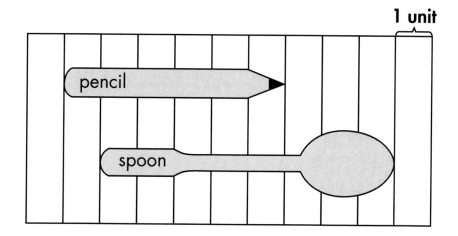

1 unit

12. The pencil is _____ units long. [1]

13. The spoon is _____ units long. [1]

14. Write the correct number in the blank. [2]

The knife is about _____ ⎯⎯ long.

Fill in the blanks. [6]

15.

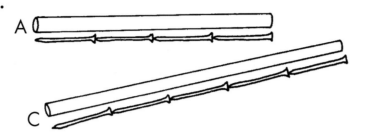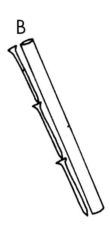

Rod A is about _____  long.
Rod B is about _____ long.
Rod C is about _____ long.
Rod A is longer than Rod _____.
Rod A is shorter than Rod _____.
Rod _____ is the shortest.

16. [6]

The glass is about _____ tall.

The bottle is about _____ tall.

The _____ is taller than the _____.

17.

pen

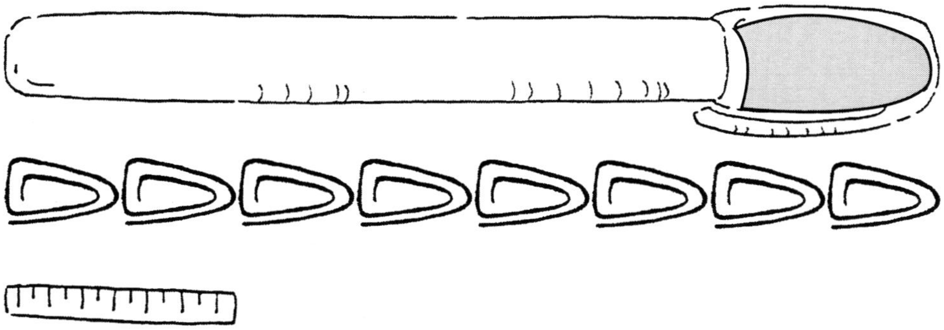

[6]

The pen is about _____ long.

The pen is about _____ long.

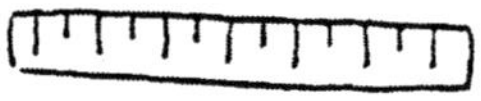

The pen top is about _____ long.

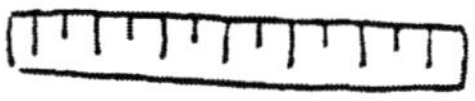

The pen top is about _____ long.

Notes

Concept: Comparing Weights

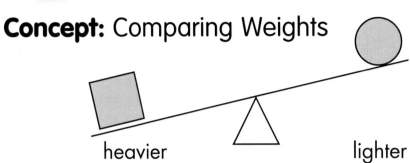

heavier   lighter

Concept: Comparing Three Weights

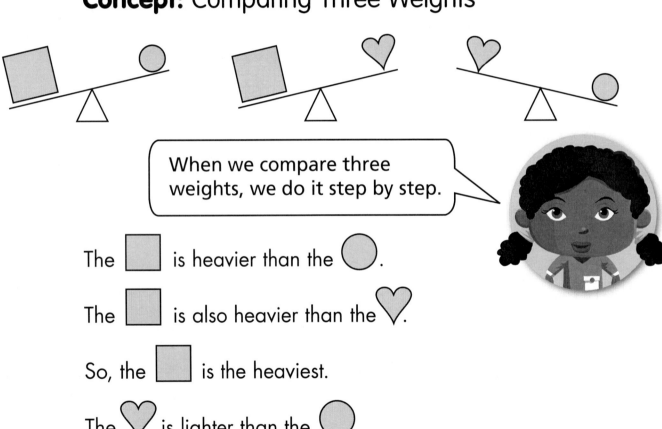

When we compare three weights, we do it step by step.

The ⬜ is heavier than the ⭕.

The ⬜ is also heavier than the ♥.

So, the ⬜ is the heaviest.

The ♥ is lighter than the ⭕.

So, the ♥ is the lightest.

The ⭕ is in the middle.

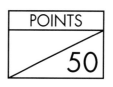
Concept: Counting Up from the Greater Number

1. Color the heavier item. [2]

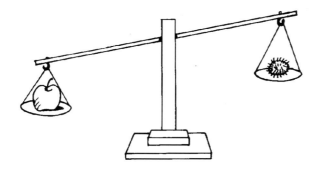

2. Color the lighter item. [2]

3. Fill in the blanks. [2]

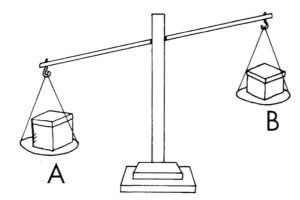

Box _____ is lighter than Box _____.

Fill in the blanks with the correct numbers.

4.   [2]

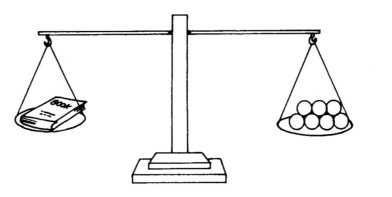

The weight of the book is about _____ ◯.

5.   [2]

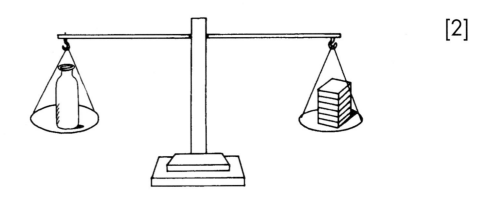

The weight of the bottle is about _____ .

6.   Color the heavier item.   [2]

A pail of water   A cup of water

7. Fill in the blanks.   [7]

Use 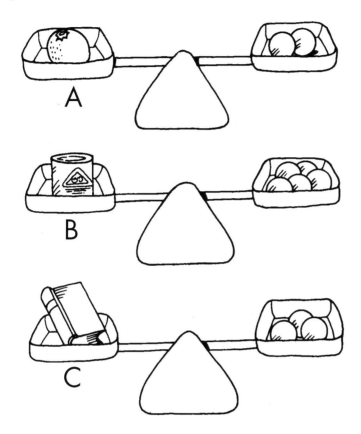 as 1 unit.

(a) The weight of item A is about _____ units.

(b) The weight of item B is about _____ units.

(c) The weight of item C is about _____ units.

(d) Item _____ is lighter than item C.

(e) Item _____ is heavier than item C.

(f) Item _____ is the lightest.

(g) Item _____ is the heaviest.

Math Practice the Singapore Way

8. Fill in the blanks.   [5]

Use 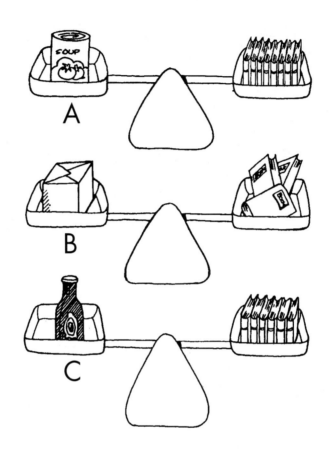 as 1 unit.

(a) The weight of item _____ is about 6 .

(b) The weight of item _____ is about 8 .

(c) The weight of item C is more than the weight of item _____.

(d) Item _____ is the heaviest.

(e) Item _____ is the lightest.

9. Fill in the blanks. [2]

    (a) What is the weight of Box B? o is 1 unit.

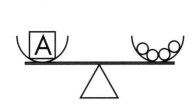 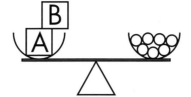

    The weight of Box B is _____.

    (b)  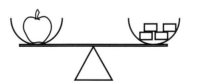 [2]

    Item _____ is lighter than item _____.

10. Look at the pictures.
    Fill in the blanks with o or ▫.

    (a) 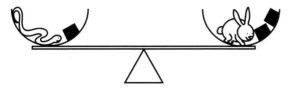 [2]

    A _____ is heavier than a _____.

    (b) [2]

    Which is lighter, the snake or the rabbit?
    The _____ is lighter.

11. Fill in the blanks. [5]

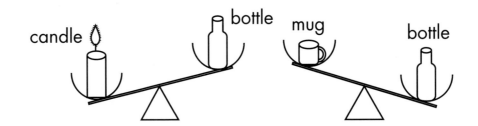

(a) The _____ is heavier than the bottle.

(b) The _____ is lighter than the bottle.

(c) Arrange the items in order.

_____   _____   _____
lightest

12. Look at the pictures. [5]

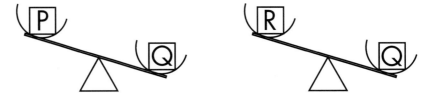

Arrange the weights P, Q, and R, in order.

_____   _____   _____
heaviest

13. Fill in the blanks.

[8]

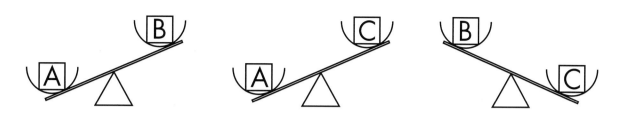

(a) Box _____ is lighter than Box C.

(b) Box _____ is the heaviest.

(c) Box _____ is the lightest.

(d) Box C is lighter than Box _____ .

Concept: Reading a Graph

The Weather for Last Week

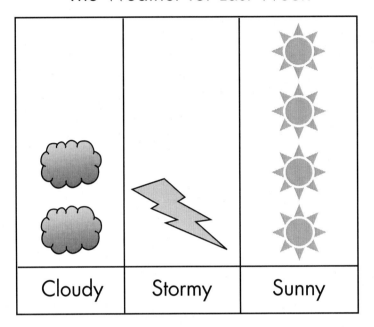

| Cloudy | Stormy | Sunny |

Graphs tell us a story.

This graph tells us what the weather was like last week.

There were 2 cloudy days, 1 stormy day, and 4 sunny days.

Most of the days were sunny.

There were fewer stormy days than cloudy days.

Graphs and Pictures

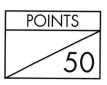

1. The pictures below show the number of pets that Geno keeps. [10]

Cat	Bird	Fish

Count the pets and complete the graph below, by coloring the correct number of boxes for the pets that Geno keeps.

Each [   ] stands for 1 pet.

Geno's Pets

Cat	Bird	Fish

2. The pictures below show the number of eggs in each basket. [10]

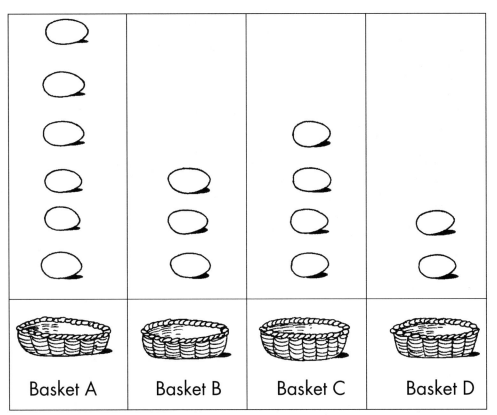

| Basket A | Basket B | Basket C | Basket D |

Count the eggs above each basket and complete the graph below.

Number of Eggs in Each Basket

Basket A	
Basket B	
Basket C	
Basket D	
Each △ stands for 1 egg.	

3. The picture graph below shows the fruit in Mother's shopping basket.
    Study the graph and then fill in the blanks.

                                                                [10]

Fruit in Mother's Shopping Basket

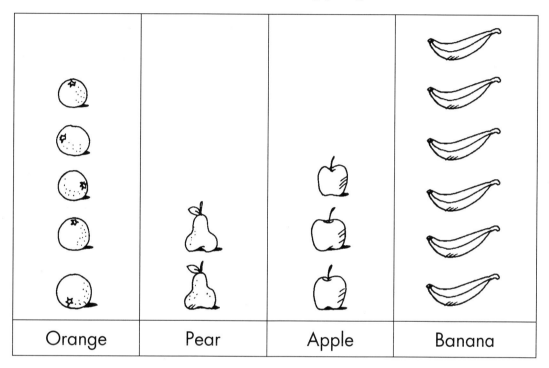

| Orange | Pear | Apple | Banana |

(a) There are _____ apples.

(b) There are _____ oranges.

(c) There are _____ bananas.

(d) There are _____ pears.

(e) There are _____ pieces of fruit altogether.

4. The graph below shows the number of toy cars that Ali, Peter, and Toby have.
Study this graph and complete the sentences.

[10]

Three Boys' Toy Cars

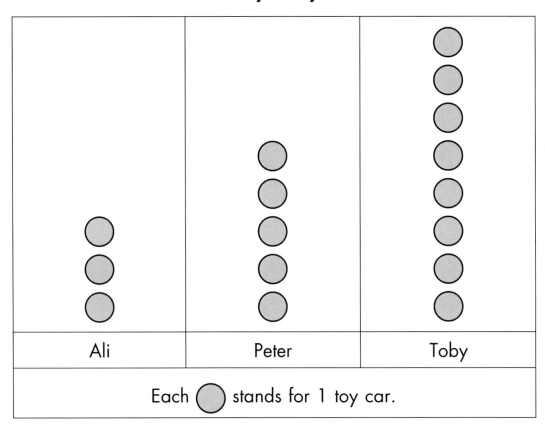

Each ◯ stands for 1 toy car.

(a) Peter has _____ toy cars.

(b) Toby has _____ more toy cars than Peter.
_____ has 3 toy cars.

(c) Toby has _____ more toy cars than Ali.

(d) Altogether the three boys have _____ toy cars.

5. The graph below shows the games that the students in Class 1D like to play.   [10]

Games Students Like to Play

Basketball	○ ○ ○ ○
Soccer	○ ○ ○ ○ ○ ○
Baseball	○ ○ ○ ○ ○ ○ ○ ○ ○ ○
Volleyball	○ ○
Table Tennis	○ ○ ○ ○ ○ ○ ○ ○

Each ○ stands for 1 student.

(a) How many students play baseball?

_____

(b) What is the least popular game? _____

(c) _____ students play table tennis.

(d) More students play soccer than basketball. How many more? _____

(e) Fewer students play volleyball than table tennis. How many fewer? _____

UNIT

Notes

Concept: Adding Mentally

17 + 2 = 19

7 + 2 = 9

10 + 9 = 19

13 + 20 = 33

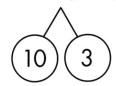

10 + 20 = 30

30 + 3 = 33

Concept: Subtracting Mentally

27 – 3 = 24

7 – 3 = 4

20 + 4 = 24

38 – 10 = 28

30 – 10 = 20

8 + 20 = 28

Mental Calculations

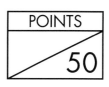

1. Think of tens and ones.
   Add mentally.   [10]

   (a) 13 + 6 = _____

   (b) 25 + 4 = _____

   (c) 31 + 7 = _____

   (d) 30 + 8 = _____

   (e) 34 + 3 = _____

   > 12 + 4 = 16
   >
   > (10) (2)
   >
   > 2 + 4 = 6
   >
   > 10 + 6 = 16

2. First look at the tens, and then at the ones.
   Add mentally.

   [10]

   > For example, 20 + 14 = 34
   >
   > (10) (4)

   (a) 20 + 14 = _____

   (b) 18 + 10 = _____

   (c) 20 + 19 = _____

   (d) 15 + 20 = _____

   (e) 10 + 23 = _____

Math Practice the Singapore Way

3. Think of tens and ones.
    Then, subtract mentally.   [10]

> For example, what is 28 – 5?
>
>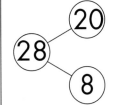
>
> Subtract the ones: 8 – 5 = 3
> Add the result to the tens:
> 20 + 3 = 23

(a) 24 – 3 = _____

(b) 29 – 6 = _____

(c) 28 – 7 = _____

(d) 37 – 5 = _____

(e) 39 – 4 = _____

4. First, look at the tens and ones.
    Then, subtract the tens.
    Next, add the tens and ones.
    Subtract mentally.   [10]

> For example, what is 36 – 20?
>
> 30
> 36
> 6
>
> 30 – 20 = 10
> 6 + 10 = 16

(a) 23 – 10 = _____

(b) 27 – 10 = _____

(c) 37 – 20 = _____

(d) 39 – 30 = _____

5. Solve the following mentally. [10]

(a)

How many
fish do I have
now? _____

(b)

How many
stamps do I have in
all? _____

(c)

How many more
oranges than apples
are there? _____

(d)

How many coins
are left? _____

Concept: Multiplying and Grouping

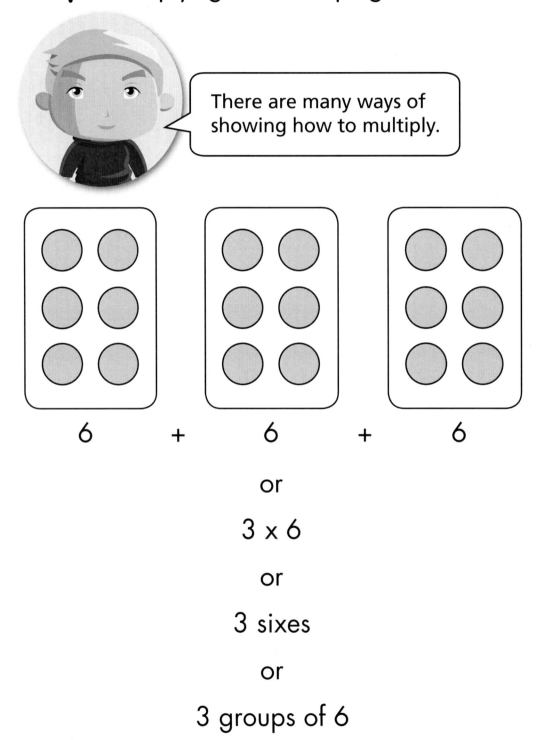

There are many ways of showing how to multiply.

6   +   6   +   6

or

3 x 6

or

3 sixes

or

3 groups of 6

1. Match the boxes that are equal. [4]

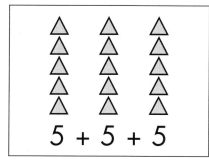

5 + 5 + 5

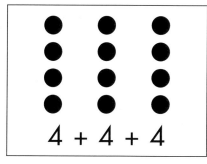

4 + 4 + 4

3 + 3 + 3

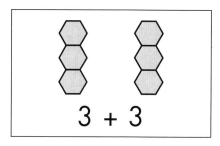

3 + 3

3 × 3

3 × 5

2 × 3

3 × 4

Math Practice the Singapore Way

2. Fill in the missing numbers. [2]

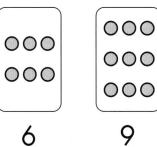 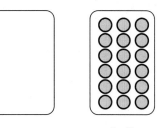

3   6   9   ____   ____   18

3. Fill in the missing numbers.

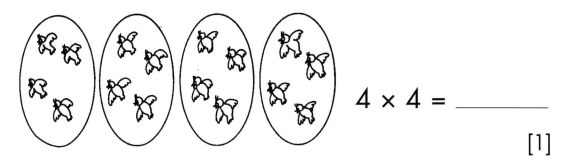

$4 \times 4 =$ _____

[1]

4. Fill in the missing numbers.

$8 + 8 + 8 =$ _____

5. Fill in the missing numbers.

$3 + 3 + 3 =$ _____

6. Draw in the rings below to show 2 fives. [2]

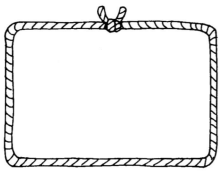 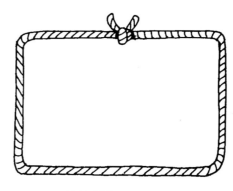

2 groups of 5 = ☐

7. Complete the following.   [2]

2 + 2 + 2 + 2 + 2 = _____

5 twos = _____

8. Count in fours. Fill in the missing numbers. [2]

| 4 | 8 | | 16 | |

9. 3 fours = _____   [1]

    5 fours = _____   [1]

Fill in the blanks.

10.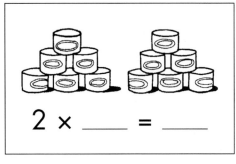

2 × ____ = ____

[2]

11.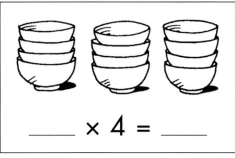

____ × 4 = ____

[2]

12.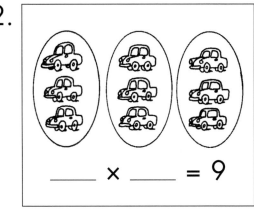

____ × ____ = 9

[2]

13.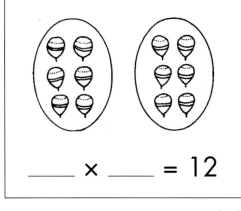

____ × ____ = 12

[2]

14. Fill in the blanks. [1]

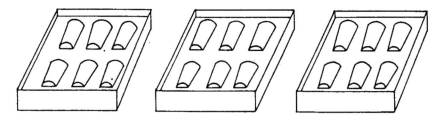

There are 3 boxes.

Each box contains 6 glasses.

3 × 6 = _____

There are _____ glasses altogether.

15.

There are 4 cages.

In each cage, there are 2 birds.

4 × 2 = _____

In 4 cages, there are _____ birds. [1]

16.

How many cups are there altogether?

3 × _____ = _____

There are _____ cups altogether. [2]

17.

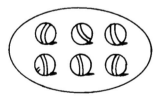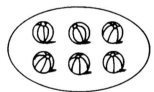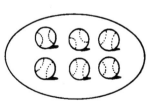

How many balls are there altogether?

3 × _____ = _____

There are _____ balls altogether. [2]

18. Write the answers in the boxes.   [4]

(a) A frog has 4 legs.

   3 frogs have ☐ legs.

   7 frogs have ☐ legs.

(b) An octopus has 8 tentacles.

   2 octopuses have ☐ tentacles.

   5 octopuses have ☐ tentacles.

19. Fill in the blanks.

   How many bowls are there? _____

   How many fish are in each bowl? _____

   How many fish are there altogether?

   _____ × _____ = _____

   There are _____ fish altogether.   [5]

20. There are 3 books.
    Each book has 8 pages.
    How many pages are there altogether?   [2]

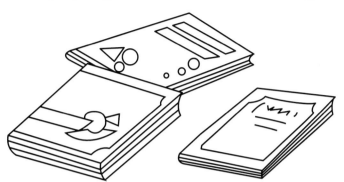

    There are _____ pages altogether.

21. Jessica has 4 pages of pictures.
    Paul has 3 pages of pictures.
    Each page has 7 pictures.

    (a) How many pictures does Jessica have?
        _____

    (b) How many pictures does Paul have? _____

    (c) How many pictures are there altogether?
        _____   [5]

Math Practice the Singapore Way

UNIT 14 Notes

Concept: Dividing and Grouping

When you divide, you put items into **equal** groups.

If I want to put 10 items into equal groups of 5, it means each group has 5.

If I want to put 10 items into 5 equal groups, it means I will divide my items into 5 groups.

Division

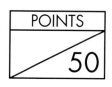
POINTS	
	50

Fill in the blanks.

1.

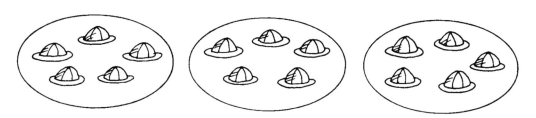

There are _____ hats in each group.   [2]

2.

There are _____ chicks in each group.   [2]

3.

  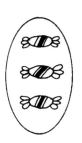 

The sweets are put equally in _____ groups.
There are _____ sweets in each group.   [2]

4.

The rabbits are put equally in _____ groups.

There are _____ rabbits in each group. [2]

5. Circle the dogs in equal groups of 3.

There are _____ groups. [2]

6. Circle the baskets in equal groups of 5.

There are _____ groups. [2]

7. Circle the oranges in equal groups of 4.

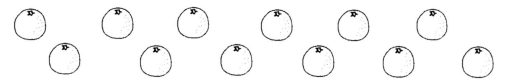

There are _____ oranges in each
group. [2]

8.

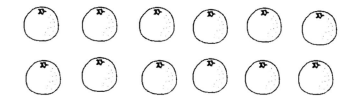

There are 12 oranges.
Mary puts 3 oranges into each basket.

She uses _____ baskets. [2]

9. Circle the toy cars in 2 equal groups.

There are _____ toy cars in each group. [2]

10.

Sam has 6 toy cars.

He puts 3 toy cars into each box.

He uses _____ boxes. [2]

11. Put 8 oranges equally into 2 groups. [3]

Draw the oranges in the rings below.

 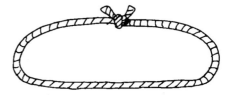

12. Put 6 oranges equally into 2 baskets. [2]

Draw the oranges in the baskets below.

13.

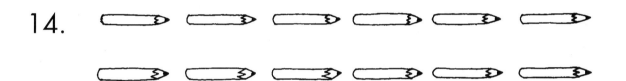

There are 15 flowers.
Put them equally into 3 groups.
There are _____ flowers in each group.   [2]

14.

There are 12 pencils.
Ann ties 6 pencils in a bundle.
She gets _____ bundles of pencils.   [2]

15.

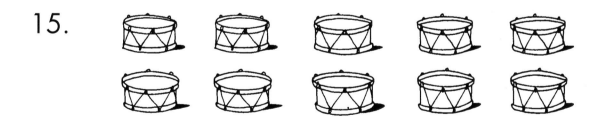

John has 10 drums.
He puts 2 drums into each box.
He uses _____ boxes.   [2]

16.

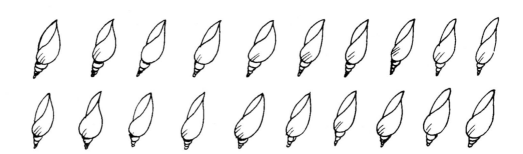

Put 20 shells equally into 4 boxes.

There are _____ shells in each box.   [2]

17.

Put 8 fish equally into 4 bowls.

Each bowl will hold _____ fish.   [3]

18.

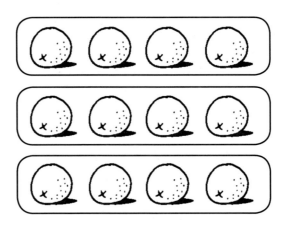

© 2012 Marshall Cavendish Corporation

(a) The oranges are put equally into _____ groups.

There are _____ oranges in each group.

(b) Ben puts 2 oranges on each plate.

He needs _____ plates to hold all the oranges.   [4]

19. Dan has 24 chickens on his farm. He puts 6 chickens into each coop. How many coops does he need?   [4]

He needs _____ coops.

20. Lisa starts out with 6 stamps. She collects 4 more stamps every week. After how many weeks will she have 34 stamps?   [6]

She will have 34 stamps after _____ weeks.

UNIT 15 Notes

Concept: Time to the Hour

When the time is exactly to the hour, the long hand points to 12 and the short hand points to the hour.

2 o'clock

5 o'clock

11 o'clock

When the time is half past the hour, the long hand points to 6 and the short hand is between two numbers. To start reading the time, choose the smaller of the two numbers.

Half past 2

Half past 5

Half past 8

Time

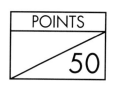
1. Match each clock with the correct time.   [16]

9 o'clock

5 o'clock

10 o'clock

11 o'clock

Half past 8

Half past 7

Half past 12

Half past 3

2. Write **Yes** or **No** in each blank.   [4]

This clock shows half past 12.

_____

This clock shows half past 8.

_____

3. Write the time shown.   [12]

_____

_____

_____

_____

4. Write the time shown. [12]

 Mrs. Li wakes up at _____.

 She eats her breakfast at _____.

 She leaves for her office at _____.

 She reaches her office at _____.

 She returns home in the evening at _____.

 She has dinner with her family at _____.

5. Write the correct time in the blanks.   [6]

John goes to lunch at _____.

He finishes his lunch at _____.

UNIT 16 Notes

Concept: Counting to 100 in Tens

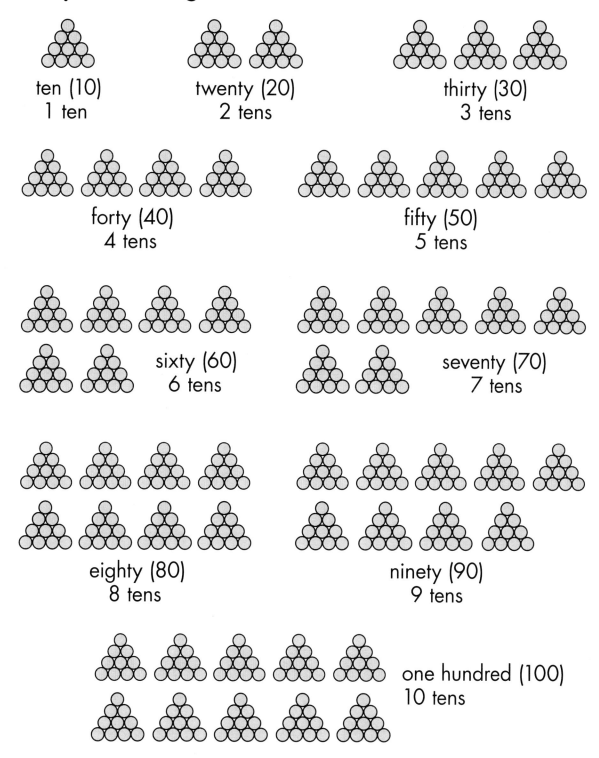

ten (10)
1 ten

twenty (20)
2 tens

thirty (30)
3 tens

forty (40)
4 tens

fifty (50)
5 tens

sixty (60)
6 tens

seventy (70)
7 tens

eighty (80)
8 tens

ninety (90)
9 tens

one hundred (100)
10 tens

Numbers to 100 (1)

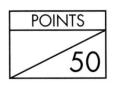
1. Count and write the correct number in the box.

[1]

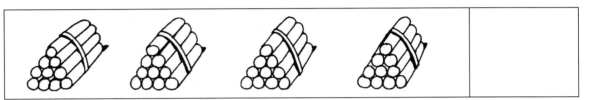

Fill in the blanks with the correct numbers.

2. 70 + 4 = _____   [1]

3. 60 + 30 = _____   [1]

4. Color 34 cans. [1]

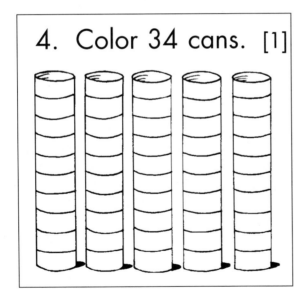

5. Color 78 small squares.   [1]

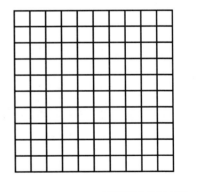

6. Circle the larger number in each set.   [2]

| 47   61 | | 86   68 |

7. Circle the smaller number in each set. [2]

86	79

54	45

Fill in the blanks.

8.  _____ oranges. [1]

9. 74 – 20 = _____ [1]

10. 48 + 20 = _____ [1]

11. 40 + 3 = _____ [1]

12. 60 + 8 = _____ [1]

13.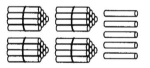

45 + 20 + 9 = _____ [1]

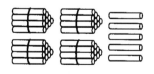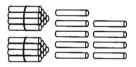

45 + 29 = _____ [1]

14. Fill in the missing numbers. [2]

57	58	59		61	62		64

15. Join the numbers in order.
    Begin with the smallest number.   [1]

    (38)   (43)

(37)   (39)   (42)

    (40)   (41)

16. Match each word to its number.   [4]

    | seventy | | 90 |

    | eighty | | 60 |

    | sixty | | 80 |

    | ninety | | 70 |

Fill in the missing numbers.   [4]

17. | 30 | 40 | | | 70 | | 90 | |

18.   [3]

    (18)(17)(16) ( ) ( ) (13) ( ) (11)(10)

19. Write the numbers in order, starting with the smallest number. [6]

(27)   (34)   (72)   (41)

_____, _____, _____, _____
smallest

The smallest number is _____.

The largest number is _____.

20. Arrange these numbers in order, starting with the smallest number. [14]

60   90   50   70

smallest

60 is greater than [   ].

70 is smaller than [   ].

Subtract the smallest number from the largest number. The answer is [   ].

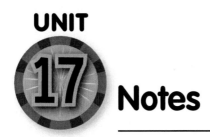
Concept: Arranging Numbers in Order

66, 42, 28, 45

When we arrange numbers, we look at the tens.
66 has 6 tens, so it is the biggest number.
28 has 2 tens, so it is the smallest number.

When numbers have the same tens, we look at the ones.
42 has 2 ones. 45 has 5 ones. So, 42 is smaller than 45.

Now we can arrange the numbers.
28, 42, 45, 66!

UNIT 17

Numbers to 100 (2)

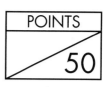

POINTS

50

1. Count and write the correct number in the box.   [1]

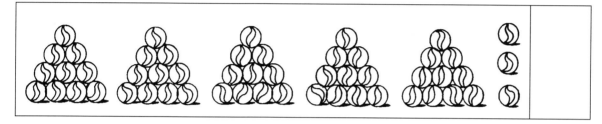

Fill in the missing numbers.

2. _____ is 1 more than 13.   [1]

3. _____ is 10 more than 13.   [1]

4. _____ is 1 less than 45.   [1]

5. _____ is 10 less than 45.   [1]

6. $18 - 3 = $ _____   [1]

7. $62 + 5 = $ _____   [1]

8. $84 - 4 = $ _____   [1]

9. $43 + 2 = $ _____   [1]

10. Circle the largest number.   [1]

| 35 | 28 | 39 | 21 |

11. Circle the smallest number. [1]

| 76 | 80 | 69 | 91 |

12. Color the correct number of squares. [1]

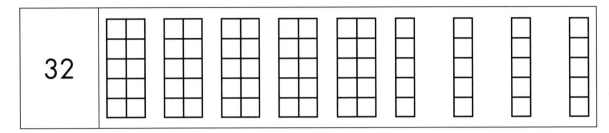

Fill in the blanks.

13.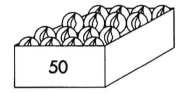

There are _____ marbles. [1]

14. 53 54 55 ⬡ 57 58 59 ⬡ 61 [2]

15. (a) 85 is 80 and _____.
    (b) 72 is _____ and 2. [2]

16. (a) 32 + 7 = _____
    (b) 53 + 4 = _____ [2]

17. (a) 49 – 6 = _____

    (b) 78 – 8 = _____   [2]

18. (a) 23 – 15 = _____

    (b) 23 – 5 = _____   [2]

19. Join the dots in order.   [1]

    46   39   40   41   44

    •   •   •   •   •

    •-----•   •   •   •
    37   38   45   42   43

20. Write these words in numbers.   [4]

    thirty-seven _____   twenty-three _____

    ninety-one   _____   one hundred   _____

21. Match each word with its number.   [4]

    | fifty-six | | 14 |
    | sixty-five | | 56 |
    | forty-two | | 65 |
    | fourteen | | 42 |

22. Match each picture with its number.   [4]

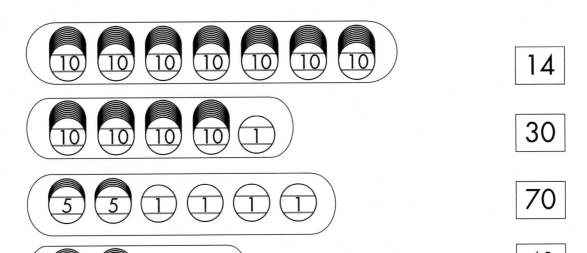

14

30

70

41

Fill in the boxes.

23. 6 tens + 4 tens = [   ] tens   [2]

24. 60 + 40 = [   ]   [2]

25. 2 tens more than 5 tens = [   ] tens   [2]

26. 80 is [   ] tens more than 60.   [2]

27. 44 + 4 = 40 + [   ] = [   ]   [4]

28. 99 comes between [   ] and 100.   [2]

Concept: Coins

There are several different coins. 1¢-coin, 5¢-coin, 10¢-coin, and 25¢-coin.

(1¢) (5¢) (10¢) (25¢)

Concept: Dollars

There are many different bills. $1-bill $5-bill, $10-bill, $20-bill, $50-bill, and $100-bill.

| $1 | $5 | $10 | $20 | $50 | $100 |

Money (1)

1. Match the money to the items.   [10]

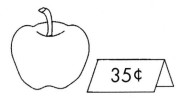 35¢

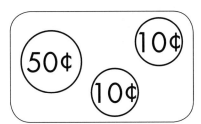

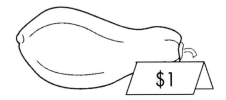 $1

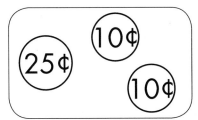

 45¢

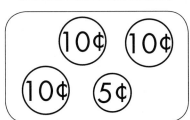

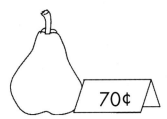 70¢

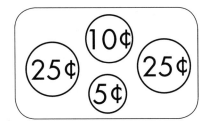

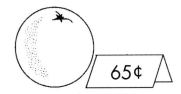 65¢

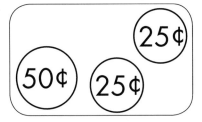

2. Color the correct amount of coins and bills. [8]

$12	$5 $5 $1 $5 $5 $1
$32	$20 $10 $5 $10 $1 $1
$26	$10 $10 $1 $50 $5 $1
$8	$10 $5 $1 $2 $2 $1

3. Check (✓) the set that has the smallest amount of money. [2]

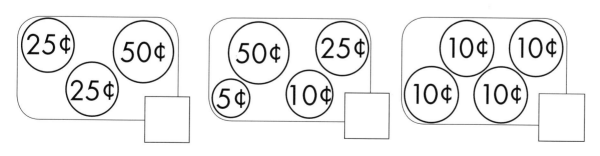

4. Write the amount of money in each blank. [16]

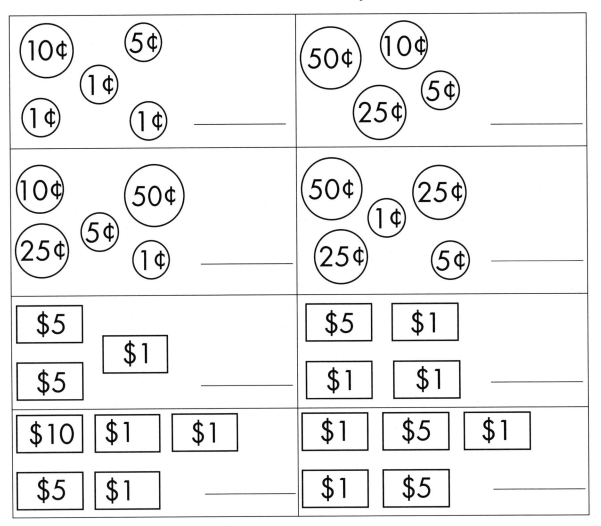

5. Color 2 coins that make up the amount shown
   on the left.   [4]

Fill in the boxes.

6. ☐ one-cent coins = 1 five-cent coin   [1]

7. ☐ five-cent coins = 1 ten-cent coin   [1]

8. ☐ one-cent coins = 1 twenty-five-cent coin

[1]

9. 1 ten-dollar bill = ☐ five-dollar bills

= ☐ one-dollar bills   [2]

10. 1 ten-cent coin = ☐ five-cent coins   [1]

11. 2 ten-dollar bills = ☐ twenty-dollar bill(s)   [1]

12. 10 one-cent coins = ☐ ten-cent coin(s)   [1]

13. 1 fifty-dollar bill = ☐ ten-dollar bills   [1]

14. ☐ fifty-dollar bills = 1 one-hundred-dollar bill

[1]

UNIT
19 Notes

Concept: Cost

cup $2

apple $1

doll $4

The cups cost $2. The doll costs $4.
2 is less than 4. So, the cup is cheaper.
4 is more than 2. So, the doll is more
expensive.

Adding money is like adding numbers.
If I have a $5 bill, what can I buy?

You can buy a cup
and an apple.
They cost $3 in all.

Or, you can buy an
apple and a doll.
They cost $5 in all.

Money (2)

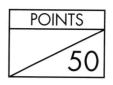

POINTS
/50

Look at the things in the box below and answer questions 1 to 5.

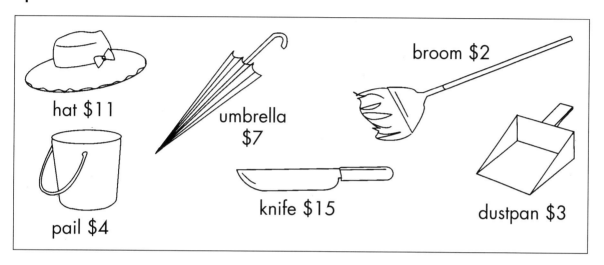

hat $11

umbrella $7

broom $2

pail $4

knife $15

dustpan $3

1. Which is cheaper, the hat or the umbrella?

   _____ [2]

2. Ali has $5.
   Which two things can he buy?

   _____ and _____ [3]

3. Miriam wants to buy a hat and a pail.
   How much money does she need to buy both?

   [ ] ◯ [ ] = [ ]

   She needs $ _____. [3]

4. Lucy has $5.
   She wants to buy the umbrella.
   How much more money does she need?

   [ ] ◯ [ ] = [ ]

   She needs $ _____ more.   [3]

5. Raj bought a pail and a knife.
   How much did he spend?

   [ ] ◯ [ ] = [ ]

   He spent $ _____ .   [3]

6. Janet has $15.
   Jack has $47.
   How much money do they have altogether?

   [ ] ◯ [ ] = [ ]

   They have $ _____ altogether.   [3]

7. Rob had $60.
   He bought a T-shirt for $22.
   How much money did he have left?

   [ ] ◯ [ ] = [ ]

   He had $ _____ left.   [3]

8. A bag of chips costs 60¢ and a sweet roll costs 35¢.

    How much do they cost altogether?

    [ ] ◯ [ ] = [ ]

    They cost _____ ¢ altogether.   [1]

9. Susan had $60. Her mother gave her $25.

    How much money does she have now?

    [ ] ◯ [ ] = [ ]

    She has $ _____ now.   [1]

10. Omar has 1 one-dollar bill.
    He gives his brother 40¢.

    How much money does he have left?

    [ ] ◯ [ ] = [ ]

    He has _____ ¢ left.   [1]

11. A teddy bear costs $40.
    A doll costs $18.
    How much more does the teddy bear cost than
    the doll?

    $$\boxed{} \bigcirc \boxed{} = \boxed{}$$

    The teddy bear costs $ _____ more than the
    doll.   [1]

12. A notebook costs 20 cents.
    A pen costs 30 cents.
    How much must Melinda pay for 1 notebook
    and 1 pen?

    $$\boxed{} \bigcirc \boxed{} = \boxed{}$$

    1 notebook and 1 pen cost _____ cents.
    Melinda must pay _____ cents for 1 notebook
    and 1 pen.   [6]

13. Louise has $13.

    She wants to buy a dress that costs $32.

    How much more does she need?

    She needs $_____ more.   [6]

14. Albert has less than $10.

    After buying a book, he has $2 left.

    Which is the most expensive book he can buy?

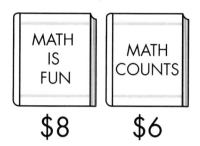

$8 $6

    He can buy the book that costs $ _____. [6]

15. A jar of peanut butter costs $2.

    A jar of jam costs $4.

    (a) How much do 3 jars of peanut butter cost?

    3 jars of peanut butter cost $ _____.

    (b) How much do 2 jars of jam cost?

    2 jars of jam cost $ _____.   [8]

Section A (80 points)

1. Count and write the numbers in **words**.   [2]

2.   [2]

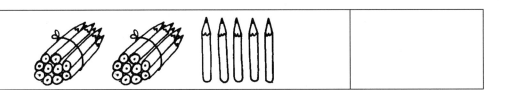

3. Cross out four ice-cream cones.   [2]

    _____ is 4 less than 9.

4. Write a number bond for the picture.   [2]

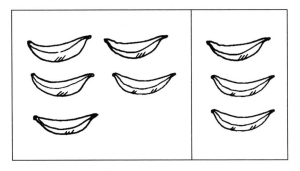   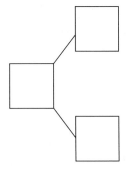

5. Count and write the correct numbers. [2]

6. Match each word to its number. [4]

thirty-nine	63
twelve	39
sixty-three	12
twenty-one	21

7. Circle the correct words. [2]

	three, thirty, thirteen
80	sixty, eighteen, eighty

8. Color the fifth fish from the right. [1]

left    right

Write the correct numbers in the boxes.

9. 36 is ☐ tens ☐ ones.   [2]

10. 4 tens is the same as ☐.   [1]

11. 72 is 1 more than ☐.   [1]

12. 72 is 10 more than ☐.   [1]

13. Color the set with the smallest sum.   [1]

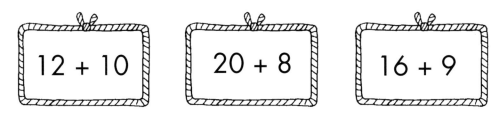

12 + 10   20 + 8   16 + 9

14. Which of the following is equal to 8?
    Circle it.   [1]

    9 + 9   14 – 6   8 – 8   3 + 4

15. Fill in the blank.   [1]

    Pitchers

    Cups

    There are more _____.

16. Draw a line to the circle that continues the pattern. [1]

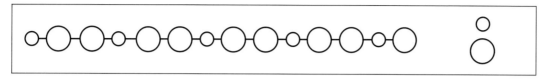

17. A square has _____ sides. [1]

18. Each  stands for 1 house. [1]

    stand for _____ houses.

19. Look at the figure and write **circles**, **rectangles**, **squares**, or **triangles** in each blank. [2]

There are 6 _____.

There are 2 _____.

20. Color the longest string of beads. [1]

 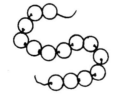 

21. Complete the sentences. [2]

A   B   C

Tree C is taller than Tree _____.

Tree _____ is the tallest.

Fill in **heavier than** or **lighter than** in the blanks for questions 22 and 23.

22. The bag of salt is _____ the bag of flour. [1]

23. The bag of flour is _____ the bag of salt. [1]

24. The weight of 1 bag of flour is the same as the weight of _____ bags of salt. [2]

25. The picture graph below shows the weights of three objects in bottle caps ( ). Use it to fill in the blanks. [2]

Weights of Objects

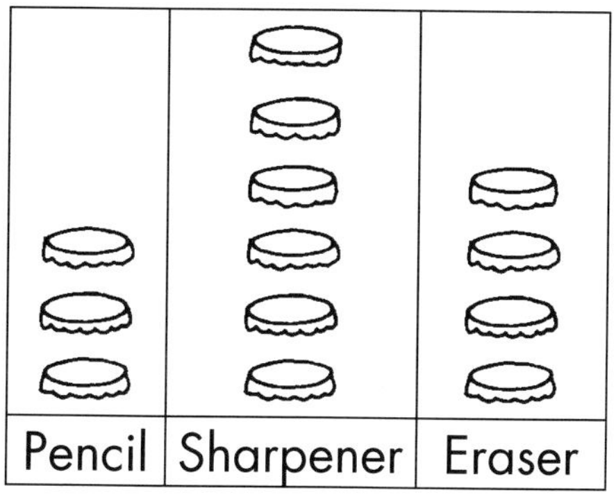

Use 1 bottle cap as 1 unit.

The eraser has a weight of _______ units.

The _______ is the lightest.

The picture graph below shows the flowers in three vases.
Study them and answer questions 26 to 28.

Number of Flowers

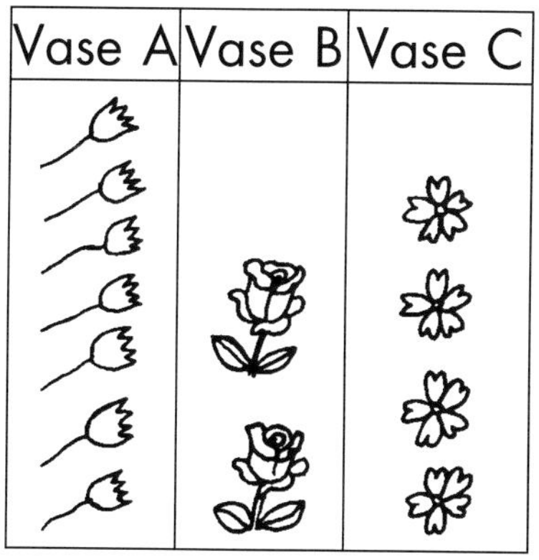

26. Vase A has _______ flowers. [1]

27. Vase B has _______ flowers. [1]

28. Vase C has _______ more flowers than Vase _______. [1]

Study the picture graph and fill in the blanks for questions 29 to 31.

Types of Shapes

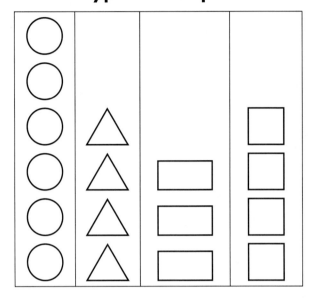

29. There are _____ circles. [1]

30. There is/are _____ more triangle(s) than rectangles. [1]

There are the same number of _____ and triangles. [1]

31. There are _____ squares and rectangles altogether. [1]

32. Draw 3 flowers () in each box.   [4]

[ ] [ ] [ ] [ ]

4 groups of 3 = _____

33. Look at the picture below.
    Then fill in the blank.   [1]

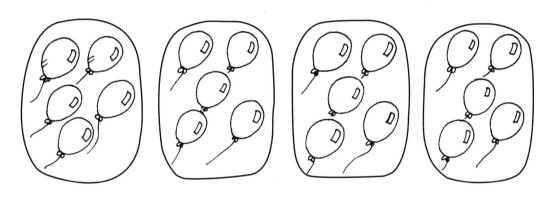

4 × 5 = _____

34. Look at the number pattern.
    What comes next?   [2]

44, 47, 50, _____

35. Fill in the missing number.   [2]

65, 55, _____, 35, 25

Math Practice the Singapore Way

36. Take away 5 tens and 4 ones from 7 tens and 2 ones. [2]

The answer is _____.

37. Draw the missing shape. [2]

△ ▢ ▯ ▭ △ ▢ _____ ▭

38. Add 25 and 7 mentally. [1]

25 + 7 = _____

39. Share 10 bananas equally among 5 monkeys. [1]

Each monkey gets _____ bananas.

40. Here are 10 flowers. [2]

Put them equally into 2 groups.

❀ ❀ ❀ ❀ ❀
❀ ❀ ❀ ❀ ❀

There are _____ flowers in each group.

41. How many boats are there? ____

Put them in equal groups of 3.
How many groups are there? ____ [3]

42. Color the correct amount and fill in the blanks. [2]

| $5 | $5 | $5 | $5 |

1 ten-dollar bill = _____ five-dollar bills.

5¢   5¢   5¢   5¢   5¢   5¢

1 twenty-five cent coin = _____ five-cent coins.

43. Match the time. [4]

2 o'clock

8 o'clock

half past 4

half past 10

44. Use the numbers and signs to write an addition
    sentence. [5]

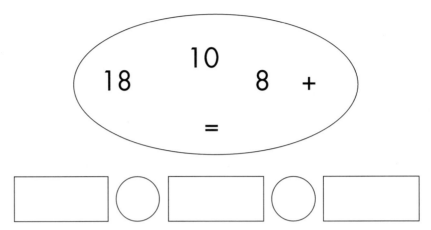

45. Fill in the blanks. [2]

    (a) 5 fours = _____

    (b) 6 fives = _____

46. Circle the two numbers that add up to 5 tens
    and 5 ones. [3]

    37   15   42   50   18

Section B (20 points)

47. Alice makes 32 burgers.

    She gives 12 burgers to her neighbors.

    How many burgers does she have now?   [4]

    She has _____ burgers now.

48. Mary has 90¢.

    She spends 35¢.

    How much does she have left?   [4]

    $$\boxed{} \bigcirc \boxed{} = \boxed{}$$

    She has _____ ¢ left.

49. There are 12 apples.

    Jennie's mother puts 4 apples in each sack.

    How many sacks does Jennie's mother have?

                                                     [4]

    She has _____ sacks.

50. Kim ate 22 grapes.

    Lucia ate 10 grapes.

    There were 40 grapes left in the basket.

    How many grapes were there at first?   [4]

    $$\boxed{} \bigcirc \boxed{} \bigcirc \boxed{} = \boxed{}$$

    There were _____ grapes at first.

51. Peter bought 2 melons at $10 each.
    He bought 4 pounds of chestnuts at $8 for
    2 pounds.   [4]

    (a) How much money did he pay for the 2
        melons?

    [   ] ( ) [   ] = [   ]

    He paid $ _____ for the 2 melons.

    (b) How much money did he pay for the 4
        pounds of chestnuts?

    [   ] ( ) [   ] = [   ]

    He paid $ _____ for the 4 pounds of
    chestnuts.

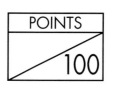

POINTS

/100

Section A (80 points)

1. Color the correct number of circles. [1]

37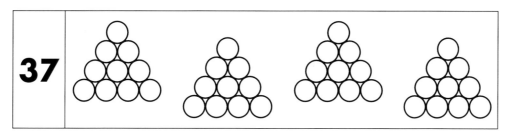

2. Join the numbers in order. [1]

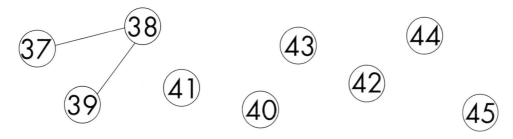

37   38
39   41   40   43   42   44   45

3. Match the number of circles to the number. [4]

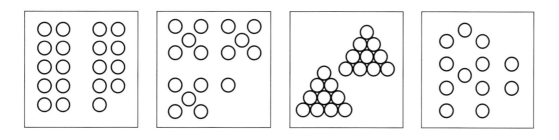

20   19   16   12

4. Write the correct amount in each blank. [2]

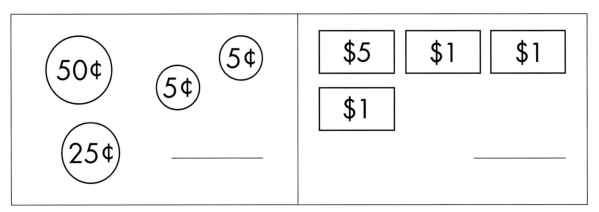

5. Write the numbers in order. [4]

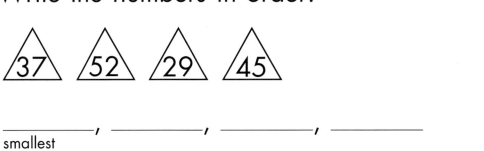

—————, —————, —————, —————
smallest

6. Draw the shape that comes next in the box. [1]

7. Color the triangle. [1]

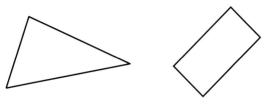

8. Circle the 3rd ship from the left. [1]

left   right

9.

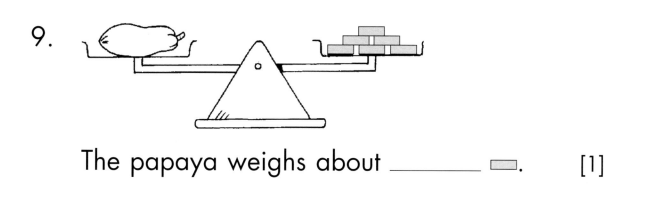

The papaya weighs about _____ . [1]

10.

The toothbrush is about _____ paper clips long. [1]

11. Study each pattern. Then draw the shape that comes next in the box. [1]

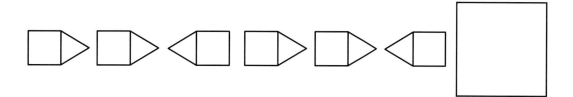

12. Fill in the missing number and draw the missing part. [1]

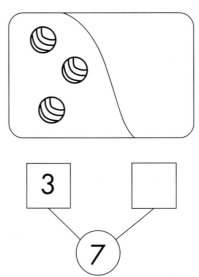

13. Write the time shown on each clock face. [2]

_____   _____

14. Write 2 subtraction sentences for this picture. [2]

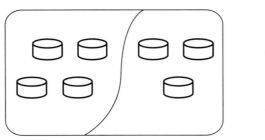

_____

_____

15. Two of the following are equal.
    Circle them.   [1]

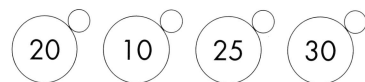

$$3 + 4 \qquad 18 - 1 \qquad 10 - 3 \qquad 2 \times 3$$

16. Color any two numbers that equal 30.   [1]

20   10   25   30   5

17. Color the set with the smallest sum.   [1]

| 19 + 7 | 8 + 11 | 20 + 1 | 16 + 2 |

18. Fill in the blanks.   [2]

Box A   Box B

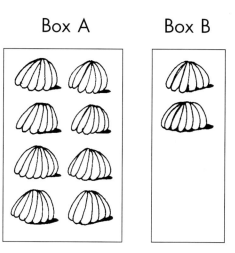

Box _____ contains more shells.

It contains _____ more shells.

19. Count in fives and fill in the missing numbers.

[2]

| 10 | 15 | | 25 | | 35 |

20. Write **+** or **−** in the circles. [2]

30 $\bigcirc$ 3 = 33

40 $\bigcirc$ 7 = 33

21. Add the following mentally. [2]

4 + 6 = _____

14 + 6 = _____

22. Write the numbers in order. Begin with the number in the first box on the right. [3]

The diagram below shows 3 baskets filled with apples.

Basket A   Basket B   Basket C

Count the number of apples in each basket and complete this graph.

Basket A	🍎 🍎 🍎 🍎 🍎	
23. Basket B		[2]
24. Basket C		[2]

25. Basket _____ has the most apples.   [2]

26. Basket _____ has the least apples.   [2]

27. Basket B has _____ more apples than Basket C.   [2]

28. Basket A has _____ fewer apple(s) than Basket B.   [2]

29. There are _____ apples altogether.   [2]

Study the graph and fill in the blanks.

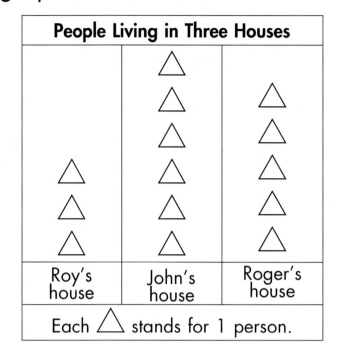

People Living in Three Houses

Each △ stands for 1 person.

30. In Roy's house, there are _____ persons. [2]

31. In Roger's house, there are _____ persons. [2]

32. Altogether there are _____ persons in the three houses. [2]

33. Fill in the missing numbers. [2]

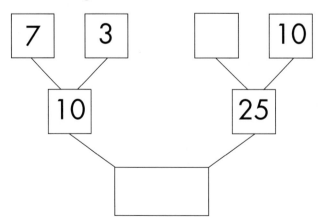

34. Circle 10 balls and fill in the boxes. [2]

$9 + 4 = 10 + \boxed{}$

$= \boxed{}$

35. Draw to show 2 × 5. [3]

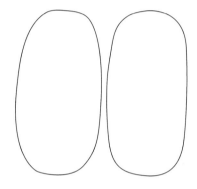

2 fives = _____

2 × 5 = _____

36. Fill in the correct numbers. [2]

$4 + 4 + 4 = \boxed{}$

$3 \times 4 = \boxed{}$

37. Circle groups of 3. [2]

There are _____ groups of 3.

38. Count the number of buttons below.   [6]

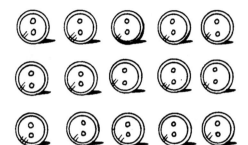

How many buttons are there altogether?

_____

Put them in groups of 5 buttons.

How many groups are there? _____

39. Jack has 24 sweets.

He wants to pack them equally into 6 bags.

How many sweets are there in each bag?   [6]

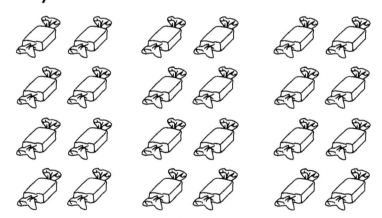

There are _____ sweets in each bag.

Section B (20 points)

40. There are 8 boys and 5 girls playing in the garden.

    How many more boys than girls are there? [4]

    There are _____ more boys than girls.

41. Elaine bought 28 cupcakes and 34 cookies for a birthday party.

    How many fewer cupcakes than cookies did she buy? [4]

    She bought _____ fewer cupcakes than cookies.

42. Mary has 68 books.

    Twenty-four are English books.

    How many books are non-English books? [4]

    She has _____ non-English books.

43. Angelina has $55.

John has $20 more than Angelina.

How much does John have? [4]

$$\boxed{} \enspace \bigcirc \enspace \boxed{} \enspace = \enspace \boxed{}$$

John has $ _____ .

44. Raju has 6 bags of marbles.

There are 5 marbles in each bag.

There are 3 red marbles in each bag.

The rest are blue marbles. [4]

(a) How many marbles does he have altogether?

$$\boxed{} \enspace \bigcirc \enspace \boxed{} \enspace = \enspace \boxed{}$$

He has _____ marbles altogether.

(b) How many blue marbles does he have altogether?

$$\boxed{} \enspace \bigcirc \enspace \boxed{} \enspace = \enspace \boxed{}$$

He has _____ blue marbles altogether.

Answers

Unit 1 NUMBERS TO 10

1.

2.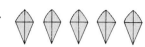

3.

4.

5.

6. 10

7. 9

8.

9.

10.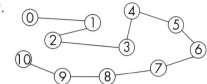

11.

12.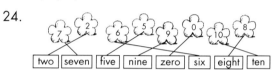

13.

14.

15. 6

16. 10

17. 1

18. 8, 7

19.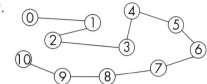

20. 8

21. 0

22.

23. 4, 2, 3, 5

24.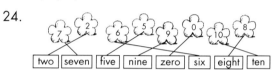

25. 5, 4, 2, 1

26. 7, 6

27.  28.

29. hands, gloves   30. 5, 5

   gloves, hands

   rabbits (or carrots),

   carrots (or rabbits), same

31. (a) 7   (b) 7   (c) 6   (d) 10   (e) 7   (f) 5

Unit 2 NUMBER BONDS

1.

🍎	🍎
3	4
4	3
5	2
6	1

2.

3.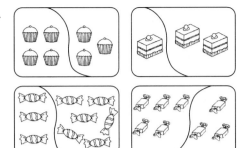

4.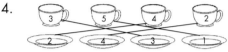

5.

6.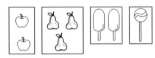

7. 3, 4

8.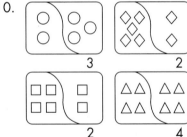

9. (a) 4   (b) 5   (c) 2   (d) 6

10.

11. (a) 6 → 2, 4   (b) 8 → 5, 3

    (c) 7 → 3, 4   (d) 12 → 6, 6

12. (a) 1, 6; 4, 3;   (b) 1, 8; 5, 4;
        2, 5; 5, 2;   2, 7; 6, 3;
        3, 4; 6, 1;   3, 6; 7, 2;
        any 1   4, 5; 8, 1;
                                  any 1

(c) 1, 9; 6, 4;
    2, 8; 7, 3;
    3, 7; 8, 2;
    4, 6; 9, 1;
    5, 5
    any 1

13. (a) 1, 7 (b) 2, 6 (c) 3, 5 (d) 4, 4 (e) 0, 8

Unit 3   ADDITION WITHIN 10

1. (a) 3, 7   (b) 3, 9   2. 4, 3, 2, 5

3. 5 + 3   4. (a) 7 (b) 7
                            (c) 8 (d) 10

5. 5 + 3, 8   6. (a) 6, 2, 8, 8
   7 + 2, 9   (b) 3, 9 → 3, 6
   4 + 4, 8
   6 + 3, 9

7. 6 + 4   7 + 3

8. (a) 3, +, 4, =, 7 or (b) 6, +, 4, =, 10 or
       4, +, 3, =, 7   4, +, 6, =, 10

9. (a) 2, 3, 2, 3, 5, 5
   (b) 4, 3, 4, +, 3, =, 7, 7
   (c) 4, 3, 4, +, 3, =, 7, 7
   (d) 6, 4, 6, +, 4, =, 10, 10

10. 3, 5, 3, +, 5, =, 8, 8

11. 4 + 1 = 5   4 + 5 = 9

    They have 9 pairs of socks altogether.

12. 3 + 2 + 3 = 8 Moses has 8 rabbits now.

Unit 4   SUBTRACTION WITHIN 10

1. (a) 2 (b) 5   2. (a) 4, 3 (b) 2, 5

3. 7 – 2   4. 7 – 3, 4
                          10 – 5, 5
                          9 – 4, 5
                          10 – 3, 7

5. 7 – 3   9 – 5   6. 7, 3, 4 7 → 3, 4

7. (a) 5, 4, 5   8. (a) 8, 3, 8, –,
   (b) 7, 7, 1, 6   3, =, 5, 5
   (c) 0, 5, 0, 5   (b) 9, 5, 9, –,
                            5, =, 4, 4

9. 6, –, 4, 2, 2   10. 7, –, 2, 5, 5

11. 8, –, 6, 2, 2

12. 4, 3, 7, 7, 3, 4, 3, 4, 7, 7, 4, 3

13. (a) 8, 8 (b) 7, 7 (c) 7, 7

Unit 5 SHAPES AND PATTERNS

1.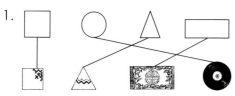

2.

3.

4. ⚠✓, ⊘

5. ▷ ◁, 2

6. ■ ◆, 2

7. ● ○ ○ ● ○

8. ● ○ ▲ △

9. triangle rectangle square circle

10. ○ □ □ ○ ■ ●

11.

Shape	Number
circle	2
rectangle	4
square	2
triangle	3

13. △✓

14. ✓

15. ✓

16. ⊘

17. (a) triangle   (b) square
    (c) circle   (d) rectangle
    (e) triangle

18. (a) ✓ / cube   (b) ✓ / cube

19. (a) ✓ / cone   (b) ✓ / cube

20. 7, 4, 3, rectangles, 16

Unit 6 ORDINAL NUMBERS

1. 1st

2. 1st

3. 1st

4. 1st

5. 1st

6. 1st

7.

8.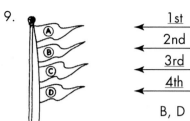

9.
B, D

10.

3rd   1st   4th   2nd

11.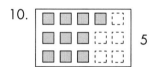

12.
4th   1st   5th   3rd   2nd

13. A, A, D, C

14. (a) 6th   (b) Joe
    (c) Ruth   (d) Ruth
    (e) Joe   (f) Alice
    (g) Paul   (h) 6
    (i) Jean   (j) Joe

15. 7

16. (a)

    (b) square

    (c)

    (d) 8th

    (e) 10th

Unit 7 NUMBERS TO 20

1.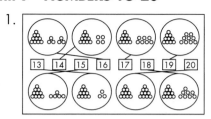

2. (a) 3 6
   (b) 19 14

3. eighteen zero fourteen nineteen sixteen
   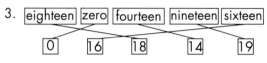
   0   16   18   14   19

4. 20, 13, 15, 12   5. 9, 12, 12, 14, 16

6. 17, 18, 19, 20   7. ⑭, ⑱

8. ⑱

9.   3

10.   5

11.   4, 14

12. ⑩ ⑩ ⑤ ⑤ ① ① ① ①

13. 2, 12   14. B, A, 8, B

15. 17   16. 18

17. 1, 2   18. 2, 0

19. (a) 14   (b) 20

20. (a) 11, 17   (b) 15, 13   (c) 12, 8
    (d) 12, 18   (e) 4, 16

21. Jason, 2

Unit 8 ADDITION AND SUBTRACTION WITHIN 20

1. 16, 18, 16, 18, 10, 12, 7, 3, 12

2. (a) –   (b) +   (c) +   (d) –
    (e) +   (f) +   (g) –   (h) –

3.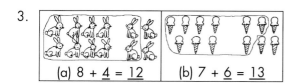
(a) 8 + <u>4</u> = <u>12</u>   (b) 7 + <u>6</u> = <u>13</u>

4.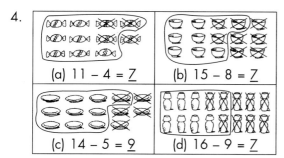
(a) 11 – 4 = <u>7</u>   (b) 15 – 8 = <u>7</u>
(c) 14 – 5 = <u>9</u>   (d) 16 – 9 = <u>7</u>

5.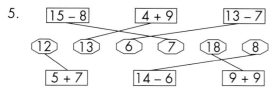

6. (a) 14 (b) 6 (c) 14 (d) 5 (e) 14 (f) 8
(g) 12 (h) 8

7. 14, –, 8, 6, 6   8. 9, +, 7, 16, 16

9. 15, –, 6, –, 2, 7, 7

Unit 9   LENGTH

1.

2.

3.

4.

5.

6.

7.   8.

9.    10.

11. (a) taller   (b) shortest
    (c) shorter   (d) tallest

12. 6   13. 8

14. 6   15. 4, 3, 5, B, C, B

16. 3, 9, bottle, glass   *17. 8, 4, 2, 1

Unit 10   MASS

1.    2.

3. B, A   4. 7

5. 6   6.
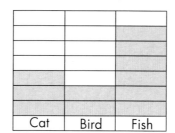

7. (a) 2 (b) 5 (c) 3 (d) A (e) B (f) A (g) B

8. (a) C (b) A (c) B (d) A (e) B

9. (a) 3 O/units   (b) P, Q

10. (a) □, O   (b) rabbit

11. (a) candle   (b) mug   (c) mug, bottle, candle

12. Q, R, P

13. B, A, B, A

Unit 11   GRAPHS AND PICTURES

1.   Geno's Pets

Cat	Bird	Fish

2.

Number of Eggs in Each Basket

Basket A	△ △ △ △ △
Basket B	△ △ △
Basket C	△ △ △ △
Basket D	△ △
Each △ stands for 1 egg.	

3. (a) 3   (b) 5   (c) 6   (d) 2   (e) 16

4. (a) 5   (b) 3, Ali   (c) 5   (d) 16

5. (a) 10 (b) Volleyballl (c) 8 (d) 2 (e) 6

Unit 12   MENTAL CALCULATIONS

1. (a) 19   (b) 29   (c) 38   (d) 38   (e) 37

2. (a) 34   (b) 28   (c) 39   (d) 35   (e) 33

3. (a) 21   (b) 23   (c) 21   (d) 32   (e) 35

4. (a) 13   (b) 17   (c) 17   (d) 9

5. (a) 9   (b) 32   (c) 14   (d) 24

Unit 13   MULTIPLICATION

1.
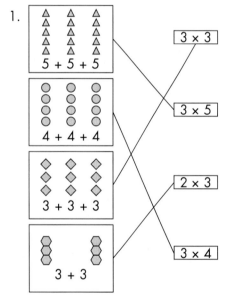

2. 12, 15   3. 16

4. 24   5. 9, 3, 9

6.
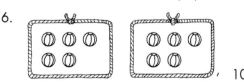
, 10

7. 10, 10   8. 12, 20

9. 12, 20   10. 6, 12

11. 3, 12   12. 3, 3

13. 2, 6   14. 18, 18

15. 8, 8   16. 4, 12, 12

17. 6, 18, 18   18. (a) 12, 28

                           (b) 16, 40

19. 2, 7, 2, 7, 14, 14

20. 24   21. 28, 21, 49

Unit 14   DIVISION

1. 5   2. 2

3. 4, 3   4. 3, 4

5.

, 4

6.

, 2

7.

, 4

8. 4

9.

, 2

10. 2

11. [peapod image]

12. [basket image]

13. 5   14. 2

15. 5   16. 5

17. 2   18. (a) 3, 4 (b) 6

19. 4   20. 7

Unit 15 TIME

1.

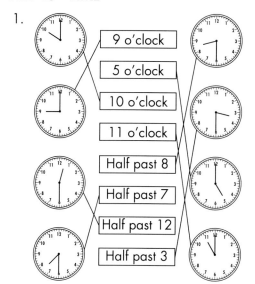

2. No, Yes

3. Half past 1,
    11 o'clock,
    5 o'clock,
    Half past 9

4. 6 o'clock, 7 o'clock, 8 o'clock, half past 9,
    half past 5, half past 7

5. 2 o'clock, half past 2

Unit 16 NUMBERS TO 100 (1)

1. 40
2. 74
3. 90

4.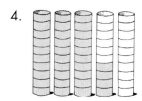
5.

6. (61)   (86)

7. (79)   (45)

8. 50   9. 54

10. 68   11. 43

12. 68   13. 74, 74

14. 60, 63

15.

16.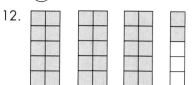

17. 50, 60, 80, 100   18. 15, 14, 12

19. 27, 34, 41, 72, 27, 72

20. 50, 60, 70, 90, 50, 90, 40

Unit 17 NUMBERS TO 100 (2)

1. 53   2. 14
3. 23   4. 44
5. 35   6. 15
7. 67   8. 80
9. 45   10. (39)
11. (69)
12.

13. 80   14. 56, 60
15. (a) 5 (b) 70   16. (a) 39 (b) 57
17. (a) 43 (b) 70   18. (a) 8 (b) 18
19.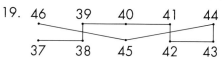

20. 37, 23, 91, 100

21.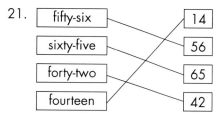

22.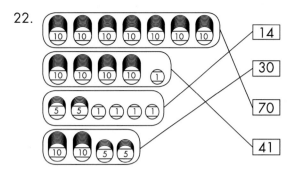

23. 10   24. 100
25. 7   26. 2
27. 8, 48   28. 98

Unit 18   MONEY (1)

1.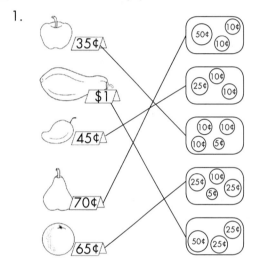

2.

$5	$5	$1	$1
$20	$10	$1	$1
$10	$10	$5	$1
$5	$1	$1	$1

3.

4. 18¢, 90¢, 91¢, $1.06, $11, $8, $18, $13
5. 50¢ 50¢,   10¢ 10¢
6. 5   7. 2
8. 25   9. 2, 10
10. 2   11. 1

12. 1   13. 5
14. 2

Unit 19   MONEY (2)

1. umbrella
2. broom, dustpan
3. $11, +, $4, $15, 15
4. $7, –, $5, $2, 2
5. $4, +, $15, $19, 19
6. $15, +, $47, $62, 62
7. $60, –, $22, $38, 38
8. 60¢, +, 35¢, 95¢, 95
9. $60, +, $25, $85, 85
10. 100¢, –, 40¢, 60¢, 60
11. $40, –, $18, $22, 22
12. 20¢, +, 30¢, 50¢, 50
13. 19   14. 6
15. (a) $2, +, $2, +, $2, $6, 6
    (b) $4, +, $4, = $8, 8

Units 1–19   TEST YOURSELF 1

1. thirteen   2. twenty-five
3. 5
4.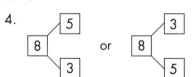

5. 13, 27
6.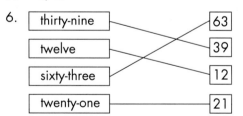

7. thirteen
   eighty

8. 🐟 🐟 🐟 🐟 🐟 🐟 🐟
9. 3, 6   10. 40

11. 71   12. 62

13. 12 + 10   14. 14 − 6

15. cups

16.

17. 4   18. 4

19. triangles, rectangles

20. 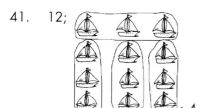   21. B, A

22. lighter than   23. heavier than

24. 2   25. 4, pencil

26. 7   27. 2

28. 2, B   29. 6

30. 1, squares   31. 7

32.  12

33. 20   34. 53

35. 45   36. 18

37.   38. 32

39. 2

40. ; 5

41. 12;

42. $5 $5 $5 $5   2   5¢ 5¢ 5¢ 5¢ 5¢ 5¢   5

43.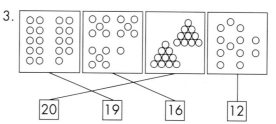

2 o'clock

8 o'clock

half past 4

half past 10

44. 8, +, 10, =, 18 or 10, +, 8, =, 18

45. (a) 20   (b) 30

46. 37, 18

47. 32, −, 12, 20, 20

48. 90¢, −, 35¢, 55¢, 55

49.  ; 3

50. 22, +, 10, +, 40, 72, 72

51. (a) $10, +, $10, $20, 20

    (b) $8, +, $8, $16, 16

Units 1–19   TEST YOURSELF 2

1.

2.

3.

4. 85¢, $8   5. 29, 37, 45, 52

6.   7.

8.

9. 6   10. 6

11.

12. ; 4

13. Half past 12, 10 o'clock

14. 7 – 4 = 3, 7 – 3 = 4

15. (3 + 4), (10 – 3)

16. 20 10   or   25 5

17. 16 + 2

18. A, 6   19. 20, 30

20. +, –   21. 10, 20

22. 18, 21, 81

23. | Basket B | 🍎🍎🍎🍎🍎🍎 |
24. | Basket C | 🍎🍎🍎 |

25. B   26. C

27. 3   28. 1

29. 14   30. 3

31. 5   32. 14

33. 15, 35   34. 3, 13

35.   36. 12, 12

 ; 10, 10

37. ; 3

38. 15; ; 3

39. 4   40. 8, –, 5, 3, 3

41. 34, –, 28, 6, 6

42. 68, –, 24, 44, 44

43. $55, +, $20, $75, 75

44. (a) 6, ×, 5, 30, 30

    (b) 6, ×, 2, 12, 12

Notes

Notes

Notes

Notes